Impact maths 1 G

About this book

Impact maths provides a complete course to help you achieve your best in your Key Stage 3 Mathematics course. This book will help you understand and remember mathematical ideas, solve mathematical problems with and without the help of a calculator and develop your mental maths skills.

Exercises you should try without the help of a calculator are marked with this symbol:

Finding your way around

To help you find your way around when you are studying use the:

- **edge marks** shown on the front pages – these help you get to the right unit quickly

- **contents list** and **index** – these list all the key ideas covered in the book and help you turn straight to them.

- **links** in the margin – these show when an idea elsewhere in the book may be useful:

There is more about fractions on page 121.

Remembering key ideas

We have provided clear explanations of the key ideas you need throughout the book with **worked examples** showing you how to answer questions. **Key points** you need to remember look like this:

■ **The distance around the edge of a shape is its perimeter.**

and are listed in a **summary** at the end of each unit.

Investigations and information technology

Two units focus on particular skills you need for your course:

- **using and applying mathematics** (unit 16) – shows you some ways of investigating mathematical problems.

- **calculators and computers** (unit 17) – shows you some ways of using calculators and computers and will help with mental maths practice.

Impact maths 1 G

10
11
12
13
14
15
16
17

Heinemann Educational Publishers
Halley Court, Jordan Hill, Oxford, OX2 8EJ
a division of Reed Educational & Professional Publishing Ltd
Heinemann is a registered trademark of Reed Educational & Professional Publishing Ltd

OXFORD   MELBOURNE   AUCKLAND
JOHANNESBURG   BLANTYRE   GABORONE
IBADAN   PORTSMOUTH NH (USA)   CHICAGO

© Heinemann Educational Publishers

First published 1999

ISBN 0 435 01761 6

02 01 00 99
10 9 8 7 6 5 4 3 2

Designed and typeset by Tech-Set Ltd, Gateshead, Tyne and Wear
Illustrated by Barry Atkinson, Barking Dog and Tech-Set
Cover design by Miller, Craig and Cocking
Printed and bound by Edelvives, Spain

Acknowledgements
The authors and publishers would like to thank the following for permission to use photographs: P1: Robert Harding Picture Library; Science Photo Library/Prof. K. Seddon & Dr. T. Evans, Queen's University, Belfast; Pet Rescue magazine, John Brown Publishing/Channel 4. P15: Corbis. P46: China Span/Keren Su. P55: Holt Studios/Nigel Cattlin. P58 and 60: Robert Harding Picture Library. P61, 62 and 63: Action-Plus/Glyn Kirk; Peter Blakeman; Neil Tingle. P91: Action-Plus/Neil Tingle. P133: Aerofilms. P162: Direct Holidays; Robert Harding Picture Library; J. Allan Cash Ltd.

Cover photo by NHPA/Stephen Dalton

Publishing team
Editorial
Philip Ellaway
Sarah Caton
Nigel Green
Gwen Allingham

Design
Phil Richards
Colette Jacquelin

Production
David Lawrence
Joanne Morgan

Author team
Tony Clough
Gareth Cole
Ray Fraser
Barry Grantham
Karen Hughes
Peter Jolly
David Kent
Christine Medlow
Graham Newman
Sheila Nolan
Keith Pledger
Ian Roper
John Sylvester

Tel:01865 888058 email:info.he@heinemann.co.uk

Contents

3   Number patterns

4   Probability

5   Multiplication and division

6 Decimals

7 Measuring

8 Fractions

9 Perimeter, area and volume

10 Formulae and equations

11 Positive and negative numbers

12 Graphs

13 Angles

14 Handling data

15 Percentages

16 Using and applying mathematics

17 Calculators and computers

Index

1 Shapes

1.1 Why do we study shapes?

The world is full of interesting shapes.

Engineers use shapes to make their structures strong ...

Designers use shapes to make the page more interesting ...

Scientists use shapes to help them understand molecular structure ...

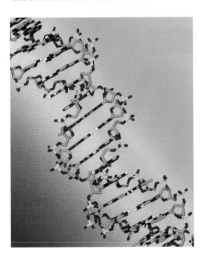

Mathematicians help us understand what is special about different shapes.

This unit introduces some shapes and shows you how to describe them.

1.2 Naming shapes

You name shapes like these by the number of sides they have:

■ Shape	Name	Hint
△	Triangle: 3 sides	**Tri**cycles have 3 wheels. **Tri**plets are 3 babies.
▱	Quadrilateral: 4 sides	**Quad** bikes have 4 wheels. **Quads** are 4 babies.
⬠	Pentagon: 5 sides	A **penta**thlon has 5 athletic events.
⬡	Hexagon: 6 sides	**Six** and he**x**agon both use the letter **x**.
⬡	Heptagon: 7 sides	A **hepta**thlon has 7 athletic events.
⯃	Octagon: 8 sides	An **oct**opus has 8 legs.

Notice that

⬡

and

⬡

are both hexagons.

1 For each shape:
   - write down the number of sides
   - name the shape.

   The first shape has 3 sides. It is a triangle.

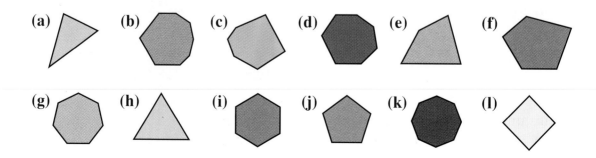

2 On this tile:

(a) how many triangles are there

(b) how many quadrilaterals are there?

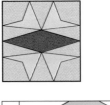

3 In this coloured window:

(a) how many pentagons are there

(b) how many hexagons are there

(c) how many heptagons are there

(d) how many octagons are there?

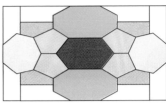

4 For each of these windows:

(a) list all the different shapes

(b) count how many of each shape there are.

(i) 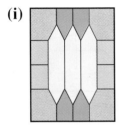 (ii) 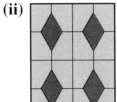 (iii) 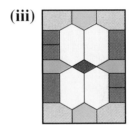 (iv)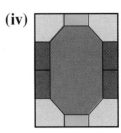

How to sketch a shape
To sketch a pentagon
draw 5 dots like this:
then join them up.

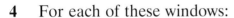

5 (a) Sketch a hexagon   (b) Sketch a heptagon   (c) Sketch an octagon
Hint: draw 6 dots

6 **Activity**   You need Activity sheet 1. Cut out the triangles and pentagons.

You can use a triangle and
a pentagon to make a
hexagon:

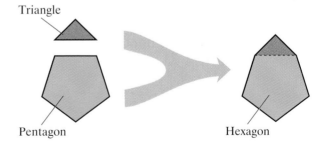

(a) Use a triangle and a   (b) Use two triangles and a pentagon to make:
pentagon to make:
- two more hexagons   - a heptagon (7 sides)
- two quadrilaterals   - a triangle
                           - a different sized pentagon

1.3 Mirror symmetry

This shape has symmetry:

This is a **line of symmetry**.

If you folded on the line of symmetry, one half would fit over the other exactly.

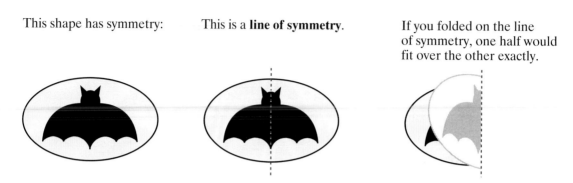

You can use a mirror to find the line of symmetry.

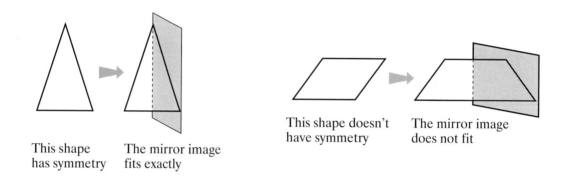

This shape has symmetry

The mirror image fits exactly

This shape doesn't have symmetry

The mirror image does not fit

■ **A shape has symmetry if you can fold it so that one side fits exactly on to the other.**
The fold line is the line of symmetry.
A line of symmetry is also called a mirror line.

Example 1

How many lines of symmetry does this shape have?

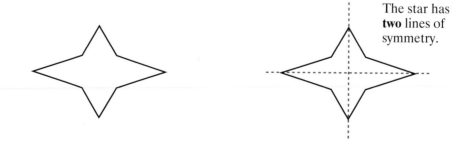

The star has **two** lines of symmetry.

Exercise 1B

1   How many lines of symmetry does each shape have?

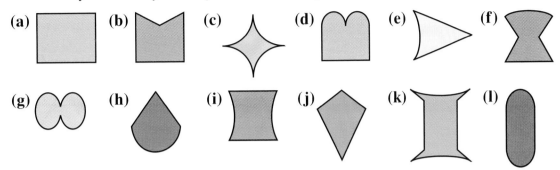

2   Copy these letters. Draw any lines of symmetry.
    The first one has been done for you.

A B C D E F H I W X N M O S

3   How many lines of symmetry do these words have?

BOB DAD WOW OXO SOS

4   What is the longest word you can find that has a line of
    symmetry? (Hint: you may need to use your
    dictionary.)

5   You need Activity sheet 2.
    Draw all the lines of symmetry on each shape.

1.4 Symmetry and regular shapes

These shapes are regular:

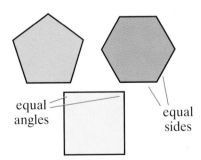

In each shape:
- the sides are equal lengths
- the angles are equal

These shapes are not regular:

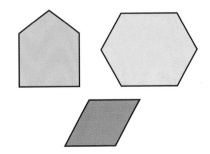

In each shape the sides and angles
are **not** equal.

■   **A regular shape has equal sides and equal angles.**

Example 2

How many lines of symmetry does
this regular hexagon have?

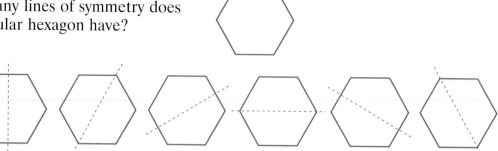

There are 6 lines of symmetry.

■ **A regular shape has the same number of lines of
symmetry as sides.**

Exercise 1C

For each shape:

● Is it regular or not regular?
● How many lines of symmetry has it got?

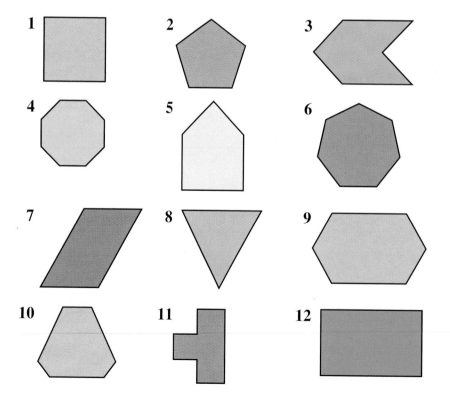

Hint: trace the
shapes into
your book first.

13 Copy and complete the sentences.
      The first one has been done for you.

  (a) A regular quadrilateral has <u>4</u> equal sides and <u>4</u>
        equal angles.
        It has 4 lines of symmetry.

  (b) A regular hexagon has _____ equal sides and _____
        equal angles.
        It has 6 lines of symmetry.

  (c) A regular pentagon has _____ equal sides and _____
        equal angles.
        It has _____ lines of symmetry.

  (d) A regular triangle has _____ equal sides and _____
        equal angles.
        It has _____ lines of symmetry.

  (e) A regular octagon has _____ equal sides and _____
        equal angles.
        It has _____ lines of symmetry.

  (f) A regular heptagon has _____ equal sides and _____
        equal angles.
        It has _____ lines of symmetry.

1.5 Reflecting shapes

You can reflect this shape in a mirror ... to make another shape:

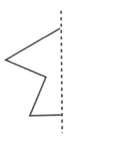
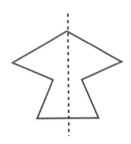

Exercise 1D

Activity You need a mirror. Use it to reflect the shapes below.

What shapes do you make?

Choose your answers from this box.

Triangle	Hexagon	Regular quadrilateral	Regular triangle
Pentagon	Octagon	Regular pentagon	Regular hexagon
Heptagon	Quadrilateral	Regular heptagon	Regular octagon

The first shape is a **quadrilateral**.

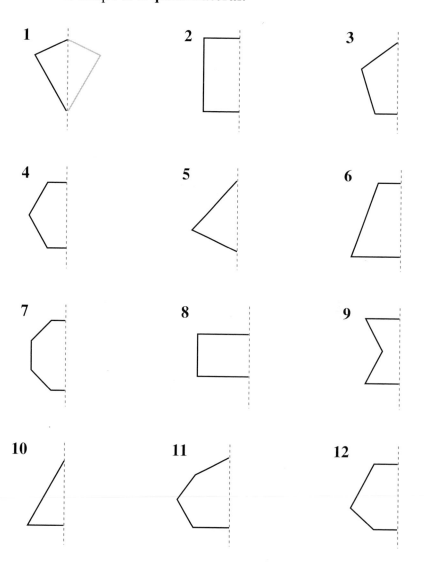

1.6 Symmetry and special triangles

Special triangles have special names:

Equilateral
All sides are equal.

Isosceles
Two sides are equal.

Scalene
No sides are equal.

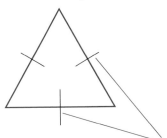

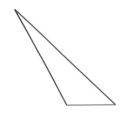

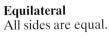

You mark equal sides with a dash.

and special symmetries:

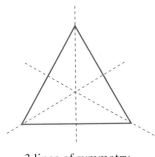

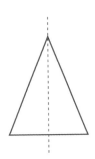

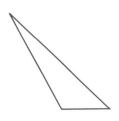

3 lines of symmetry

1 line of symmetry

no lines of symmetry

Exercise 1E

For each triangle write down:

(a) how many sides are equal

(b) the name of the triangle

(c) how many lines of symmetry it has.

1 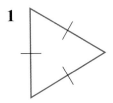 **2**   **3**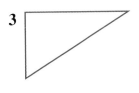

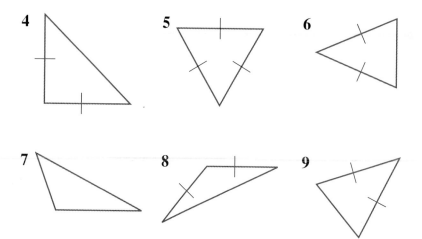

4   **5**   **6**

7   **8**   **9**

1.7 Symmetry in quadrilaterals

Sides marked with
the same number of
dashes are equal.

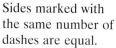

Sides marked with
the same number of
arrows are parallel.

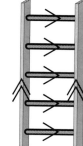

On this ladder:
the rungs are parallel
the sides are parallel

Special quadrilaterals have special names:

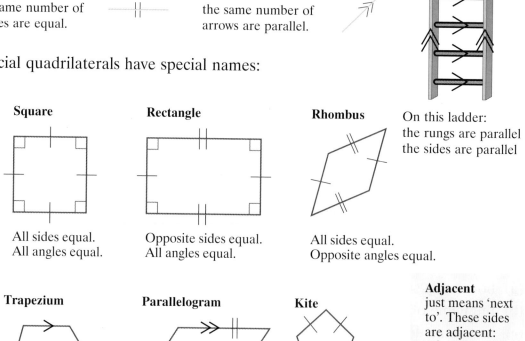

Square

All sides equal.
All angles equal.

Rectangle

Opposite sides equal.
All angles equal.

Rhombus

All sides equal.
Opposite angles equal.

Trapezium

Only one pair of
sides is parallel.

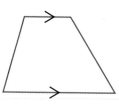

Parallelogram

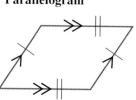

Opposite sides equal
and parallel.
Opposite angles equal.

Kite

Two pairs of adjacent
sides are equal.

Adjacent
just means 'next
to'. These sides
are adjacent:

Exercise 1F

For each shape write down:

- the name of the shape (give the reasons for your answer)
- how many lines of symmetry it has.

The first shape is a parallelogram.
Reason: Opposite sides are equal and parallel.

No lines of symmetry.

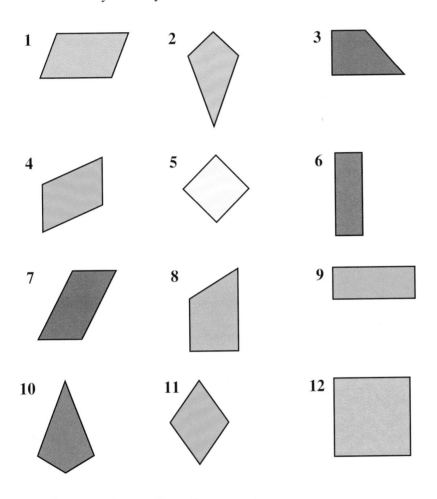

13 Copy and complete these sentences:

    (a) A quadrilateral has _____ sides.

    (b) A square has _____ lines of symmetry.

    (c) A kite has _____ line of symmetry.

    (d) A rhombus has _____ lines of symmetry.

    (e) A rectangle has _____ lines of symmetry.

    (f) A parallelogram has _____ lines of symmetry.

14 **Activity**   Use two equilateral triangles.

    (a) How many different shapes can you
        make with them?
    (b) Write down the name of any shape
        you have made.

You can trace
this equilateral
triangle.

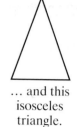

... and this
isosceles
triangle.

15 **Activity**   Repeat question **14** using:

    (a) 3 equilateral triangles   **(b)** 4 equilateral triangles
    (c) 2 isosceles triangles   **(d)** 3 isosceles triangles
    (e) 4 isosceles triangles

Make sure that:

The edges line
up like this ...

... not like this!

No overlapping
allowed.

1.8 Solid shapes

Here are four types of solid shapes.
You need to be able to recognise them.

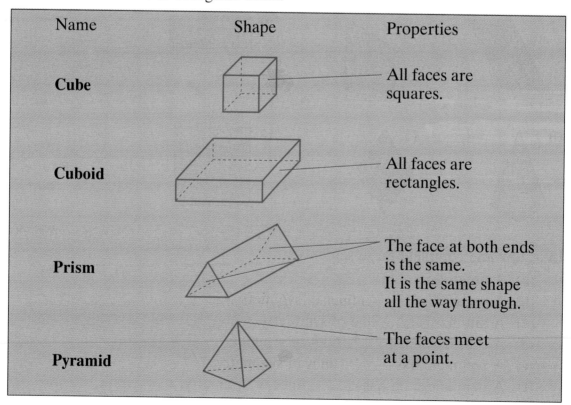

Name	Shape	Properties
Cube		All faces are squares.
Cuboid		All faces are rectangles.
Prism		The face at both ends is the same. It is the same shape all the way through.
Pyramid		The faces meet at a point.

Exercise 1G

Which of these shapes are:

(a) cubes   **(b)** cuboids   **(c)** prisms   **(d)** pyramids?

1    **2**   **3**

4   **5**   **6**

7 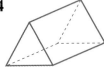   **8** 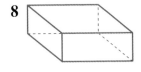   **9**

10 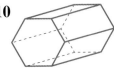   **11** 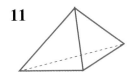   **12**

13 For each of these prisms, write down the shape of the end face.

This is the end face

(a)    **(b)** 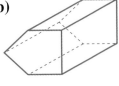   **(c)**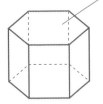

14 For each pyramid, write down the shape of the base.

(a)   **(b)**   **(c)**

1.9 Prisms and pyramids

Naming prisms

A prism is the same shape all the way through.

You can cut any prism in two like this:

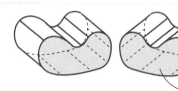

The middle of a prism looks exactly the same as the end face.

It has a **constant cross section**.

You name a prism by the shape of its cross section.

Triangular prism

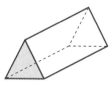

The cross section is a triangle

Hexagonal prism

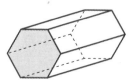

The cross section is a hexagon

Pentagonal prism

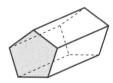

The cross section is a pentagon

Naming pyramids

You name a pyramid by the shape of its base.

Triangular based pyramid

The base is a triangle

Hexagonal based pyramid

The base is a hexagon

Square based pyramid

The base is a square

Exercise 1H

Write down the name of each shape:

1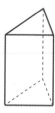
2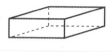
3
4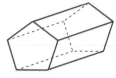

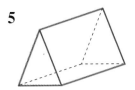

5

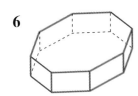

6

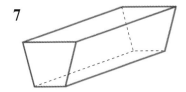

7

1.10 Plane symmetry

Some solid shapes have symmetry too.

■ **A plane of symmetry cuts a solid shape into two parts that are mirror images of each other.**

This building has plane symmetry.　This car has plane symmetry.　This wedge has plane symmetry.

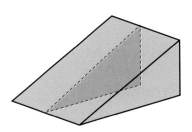

This is the plane of symmetry.

1.11 Plane spotting

A solid shape can have many planes of symmetry.

Example 3

How many planes of symmetry does this shape have?

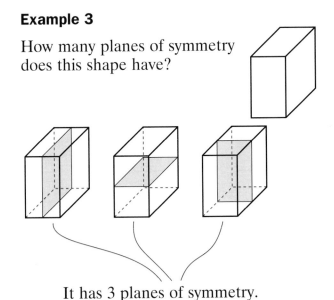

It has 3 planes of symmetry.

Example 4

How many planes of symmetry does this prism have?

Every prism has this plane of symmetry......

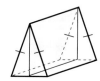

... but this prism has another plane of symmetry too.

This prism has two planes of symmetry

Pyramids

If the base has symmetry the pyramid may have plane symmetry.
It will only have plane symmetry if the top of the pyramid is above a line of symmetry on the base.

Example 5

How many planes of symmetry does this square based pyramid have?

The top of the pyramid is over one corner of the square.

The square has 4 lines of symmetry:

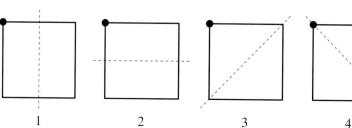

1   2   3   4

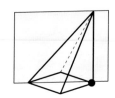

Only one line of symmetry passes through the corner.
So the pyramid has 1 plane of symmetry.

Exercise 1I

1   For each shape, write down the number of planes of symmetry it has.

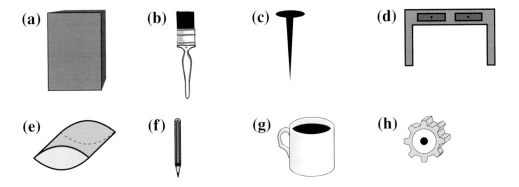

(a)   (b)   (c)   (d)

(e)   (f)   (g)   (h)

2   For each shape, write down:
   • the name of the shape
   • how many planes of symmetry it has.

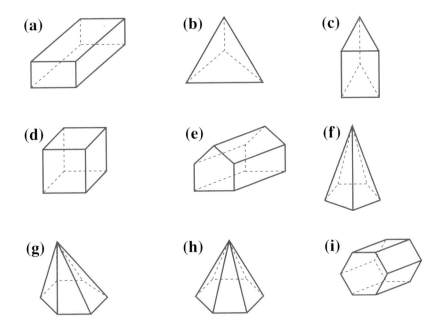

(a)   (b)   (c)

(d)   (e)   (f)

(g)   (h)   (i)

3   How many planes of symmetry does each shape in Exercise **1H** have?

Summary of key points

1	Shape	Name	Hint
		Triangle: 3 sides	**Tri**cycles have 3 wheels. **Tri**plets are 3 babies.
		Quadrilateral: 4 sides	**Quad** bikes have 4 wheels. **Quads** are 4 babies.
		Pentagon: 5 sides	A **penta**thlon has 5 athletic events.
		Hexagon: 6 sides	Si**x** and he**x**agon both use the letter **x**.
		Heptagon: 7 sides	A **hepta**thlon has 7 athletic events.
		Octagon: 8 sides	An **oct**opus has 8 legs.

2   A shape has symmetry if you can fold it so that
one side fits exactly on to the other.
The fold line is the line of symmetry.
The line of symmetry is also called the mirror line.

3   A regular shape has equal sides and equal angles.

4   A regular shape has the same number of lines of symmetry as sides.

5   A plane of symmetry cuts a solid shape into two parts that are mirror images of each other.

2 Understanding numbers

2.1 Digits and place value

Our number system was invented in India over 1400 years ago...

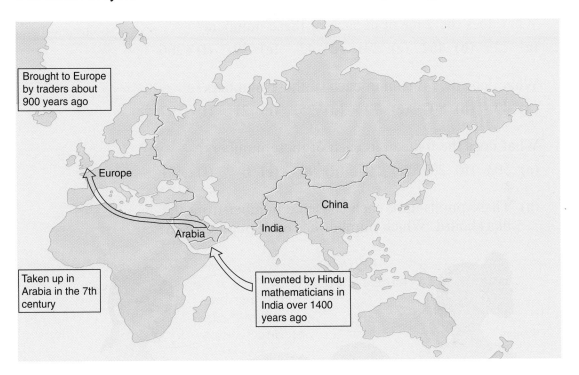

You can use it to make large and small numbers using just ten **digits**:

0 1 2 3 4 5 6 7 8 9

■ **The value of a digit depends on its place in a number.**
You can see this in a place value diagram:

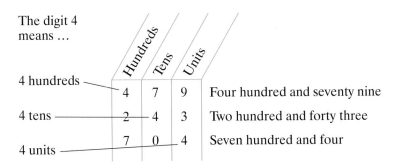

■ **82 is a two-digit number because it has two digits**
704 is a three-digit number because it has three digits

704 is also called a three-figure number.

Exercise 2A

1 What does the 2 mean in each of these numbers?
(a) 723 (b) 462 (c) 291 (d) 42 (e) 29 (f) 206

2 What does the 7 mean in each of these numbers?
(a) 47 (b) 807 (c) 79 (d) 751 (e) 71 (f) 597

3 What does the 0 mean in each of these numbers?
(a) 503 (b) 280 (c) 204 (d) 90 (e) 0 (f) 601

4 (a) These pupils have each chosen a number from the blackboard. Which number has each pupil chosen?

(b) Choose a number from the blackboard and describe it.

5   This is a machine for sorting numbers:

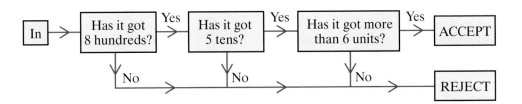

Which of these numbers are accepted and which are rejected?

(a) Eight hundred and fifty nine

(b) Five hundred and eighty nine

(c) Eight hundred and fifty seven

(d) Eight hundred and fifty five

(e) Eight hundred and fifty six

(f) Seven hundred and fifty eight

6   This is another machine for sorting numbers:

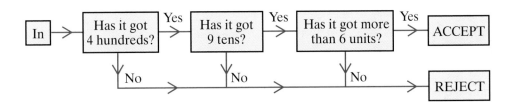

Which numbers will it accept?

7   Design a number machine to accept only these three-digit numbers

(a) 648, 649   **(b)** 390, 391, 392   **(c)** 867, 877, 887, 897

(d) 873, 973   **(e)** 721, 821, 921   **(f)** 302, 312, 322, 332

8   Design a number machine to accept these three-digit numbers only: 253, 254, 255.

Hint: you will need to ask two questions about the units.

2.2 Reading large numbers

Did you know...

You'll spend over 14 000 hours in school before you leave ...

There are about 690 000 students the same age as you in the UK ...

You'll eat over 10 000 tonnes of food in your lifetime ...

A place value diagram can help you read large numbers:

The digit 5 means ...	Hundred thousands	Ten thousands	Thousands	Hundreds	Tens	Units	
5 thousand			5	0	0	0	Five thousand
50 thousand		5	0	0	0	0	Fifty thousand
500 thousand	5	0	0	0	0	0	Five hundred thousand

You read and write large numbers like this:

67 382 Sixty seven thousand, three hundred and eighty two
324 167 Three hundred and twenty four thousand, one hundred and sixty seven

A space like this shows you where the thousands end.

Example 1

How many thousands are there in each of these numbers?

(a) 28 394   (b) 407 302   (c) 5 293

(a) 28 thousands   (b) 407 thousands (c) 5 thousands

Exercise 2B

1 How many thousands are there in each of these numbers?
  (a) 7 483 **(b)** 73 803 **(c)** 39 870 **(d)** 836 339
  (e) 8 401 **(f)** 923 458 **(g)** 873 994 **(h)** 47 824

2 How many thousands are there in each of these numbers?
  (a) 5 089 **(b)** 50 398 **(c)** 407 338 **(d)** 490 704
  (e) 120 067 **(f)** 196 383 **(g)** 587 934 **(h)** 196 038

3 What does the 6 mean in each of these numbers?
  (a) 26 277 **(b)** 365 789 **(c)** 648 925 **(d)** 960 382
  (e) 629 487 **(f)** 196 383 **(g)** 69 421 **(h)** 196 038

4 Write these numbers using digits.
  (a) Five thousand two hundred and forty six.
  (b) Forty seven thousand three hundred and ninety six.
  (c) Three hundred and sixty four thousand nine
      hundred and fifty six.
  (d) Two hundred and five thousand nine hundred and
      eighty one.
  (e) Nine hundred thousand two hundred and fifteen.
  (f) Twenty six thousand and thirty eight.

5 This is a number machine for sorting numbers with
  thousands:

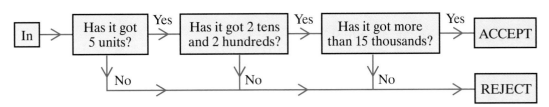

  Which of these numbers are accepted and which are
  rejected by the machine?
  (a) 14 225 **(b)** 31 225 **(c)** 140 225 **(d)** 25 252
  (e) 280 255 **(f)** 225 525 **(g)** 789 225 **(h)** 15 225

6 Design a number machine to accept these numbers
  only:
  (a) 21 507, 21 508, 21 509
  (b) 47 395, 48 395, 49 395
  (c) 899 423, 898 423, 897 423

  Hint: you will need
  to ask two questions
  about the thousands.

2.3 Order, order!

In a lottery six balls are picked.

Then they are sorted in order of size, smallest first.

You can use a number line to help sort numbers into size order.

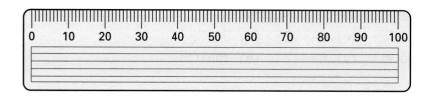

A millimetre ruler makes a good number line.

Example 2

Put the numbers 24, 97, 47, 8, 66 in order of size.
Start with the smallest number.

Find the position of each number on a number line.

So the order is: 8, 24, 47, 66, 97.

Exercise 2C

Put these numbers in size order. Start with the smallest.

1 81, 25, 4, 43   **2** 48, 96, 17, 33   **3** 94, 93, 36, 54

4 24, 38, 56, 15   **5** 50, 0, 49, 100   **6** 26, 14, 11, 84

7 98, 51, 69, 42   **8** 41, 83, 60, 7   **9** 18, 26, 54, 76

10 87, 54, 38, 11   **11** 79, 3, 99, 7   **12** 46, 20, 63, 77

13 **Activity** You need ten cards numbered:
0, 1, 2, 3, 4, 5, 6, 7, 8, 9.

Put them in a bag or a box and pick out two cards.

Can you make a number less than 50 with your two cards?

Can you make a number greater than fifty with your two cards?

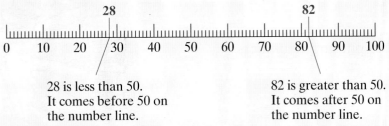

28 is less than 50.
It comes before 50 on the number line.

82 is greater than 50.
It comes after 50 on the number line.

Write down your results then put the two cards back in the bag.

Repeat the experiment until you have done it ten times.

(a) Which pairs of cards can only be used to make numbers less than 50?

(b) Which pairs of cards can only be used to make numbers greater than 50?

(c) Which pairs of cards can be used to make one number less than 50 and one number greater than 50?

(d) Are there any other possibilities?

14 **Activity** You need ten cards numbered:
0, 1, 2, 3, 4, 5, 6, 7, 8, 9.

Pick out three cards from the bag.

Make as many different two-digit numbers as you can with the three cards.

Write them down in order of size, smallest first.

Put the three cards back in the bag.

Repeat the experiment until you have done it five times.

(a) Name three cards that will only make numbers bigger than 50.

(b) Name three cards that will only make numbers smaller than 50.

(c) Name three cards that will only make numbers between 40 and 90.

2.4 Ordering large numbers

To sort large numbers you'd need a huge number line ...

Here is another way to put large numbers in order.

Example 3

Put these numbers in order of size, starting with the smallest:

392   365   589   121   633   583

First sort them using the **hundreds** digits:

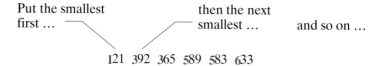

Put the smallest first ...   then the next smallest ...   and so on ...

121 392 365 589 583 633

392 and 365 both have 3 hundreds.
Sort them using the tens digits.

121 392 365 589 583 633

Put the smallest first ...   then the next smallest ...

121 365 392 589 583 633

589 and 583 both have 5 hundreds and 8 tens.
Sort them using the units digits.

121 392 365 589 583 633

Put the smallest first ...   then the next smallest ...

121 365 392 583 589 633

Now the numbers are in size order: 121 365 392 583 589 633.

Exercise 2D

Put each set of numbers in order of size, starting with the smallest.

1 533, 278, 514, 288, 233

2 876, 428, 407, 858, 849

65 has 0 hundreds

3 183, 938, 147, 958, 941

4 94, 438, 263, 488, 65

5 91, 684, 629, 392, 381

6 547, 36, 295, 216, 18

7 257, 838, 469, 472, 829, 437, 238

8 548, 485, 763, 492, 576, 559, 782

9 **Activity** You need ten cards numbered: 0, 1, 2, 3, 4, 5, 6, 7, 8, 9.

Put them in a bag or box and pick out three cards. Arrange the cards to make the largest three-digit number possible. Arrange the three cards to make the smallest three-digit number possible.

Write down your results then put the three cards back into the bag. Repeat the experiment until you have done it ten times.

(a) Write a rule to explain how to find the largest three-digit number.

(b) Write a rule to explain how to find the smallest three-digit number.

10 Write down the smallest three-digit number and the largest 3-digit number that can be made from each set of cards.

(a) 5 2 9

(b) 7 8 3

(c) 2 1 7

(d) 4 9 7

(e) 4 2 9

(f) 1 9 3

Remember: you don't write 0 at the front of a number.

(g) 8 4 1

(h) 6 7 4

(i) 2 4 3

(j) 5 8 7

(k) 7 3 7

(l) 4 8 0

11 Write down the second largest three-digit number that can be made with each set of cards.

(a) [4][3][9]   (b) [2][9][6]   (c) [3][4][0]

(d) [3][1][6]   (e) [9][8][7]   (f) [3][4][5]

(g) [7][3][4]   (h) [0][8][1]   (i) [4][2][7]

12 Write down the second smallest three-digit number that can be made with each set of cards.

(a) [5][2][9]   (b) [4][8][3]   (c) [2][5][1]

(d) [4][1][8]   (e) [6][7][8]   (f) [3][7][6]

(g) [8][7][6]   (h) [0][9][2]   (i) [3][5][7]

2.5 Mental maths

The next exercise will help you practise adding and subtracting small numbers in your head.

If you can do these you will be able to add and subtract larger numbers more easily.

 This sign next to an exercise means don't use your calculator!

Exercise 2E

You can use this number line to help you answer the questions:

| 0 | 1 | 2 | 3 | 4 | 5 | 6 | 7 | 8 | 9 | 10 | 11 | 12 | 13 | 14 | 15 | 16 | 17 | 18 | 19 | 20 |

1 Find two numbers next to each other which:

(a) add up to 7   (b) add up to 5   (c) add up to 11

(d) total 9   (e) total 15   (f) add up to 19

2 Find three numbers next to each other which:

(a) add up to 12   (b) total 6   (c) add up to 3

(d) total 15   (e) add up to 9   (f) total 18

3 Find as many pairs of numbers as you can which have a sum of:

(a) 9   (b) 12   (c) 10   (d) 15   (e) 18   (f) 20

4 Find as many pairs as you can which have a difference of:

(a) 5   (b) 8   (c) 16   (d) 20   (e) 1   (f) 10

Remember: sum is another word for the total.

The numbers do not have to be next to each other. For example 19 and 1 make 20.

5 Find as many different ways as you can to fill the square and triangular boxes.

(a) $\square + \triangle = 11$

(b) $2 + \square = \triangle$

(c) $\square - \triangle = 4$

(d) $12 - \square = \triangle$

(e) $\square - 5 = \triangle$

(f) $\square + 7 = \triangle$

(g) $\square + 2 = \triangle + 3$

(h) $20 - \square = 10 + \triangle$

For example:

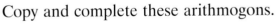

$\square + \triangle = 11$

$\boxed{4} + \triangle_7 = 11$

$\boxed{9} + \triangle_2 = 11$

6 Can you make each number from 8 to 20 by adding only threes and fives?

For example:

$11 = 3 + 3 + 5$

7 What numbers can you make by adding twos and threes?

8 Copy or trace this diagram into your book:

Write the numbers

    1, 2, 3, 4, 5, 6, 7, 8, 9

in the circles so that each line of numbers adds up to 15.

Make up your own puzzle like this.

9 This is called an arithmogon.
On each side of the triangle the total of the numbers in the circles is shown in the square.

Copy and complete these arithmogons.

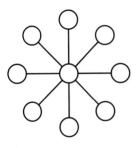

$6 + 5 = 11$

(a)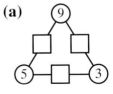

(b)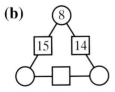

(c)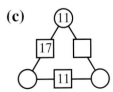

(d)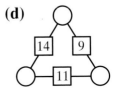

(e)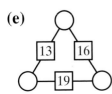

(f)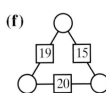

2.6 Mental maths with tens

Mental maths is easier if you can add and subtract 10 quickly.

■ **When you add 10 the units digit stays the same:**

$$8 + 10 = 18 \qquad \text{or} \qquad \begin{array}{r} 10 \\ 8\ + \\ \hline 18 \end{array}$$

■ **When you subtract 10 from a larger number the units digit stays the same:**

$$37 - 10 = 27 \qquad \text{or} \qquad \begin{array}{r} 37 \\ 10\ - \\ \hline 27 \end{array}$$

Exercise 2F

1 Activity You need a calculator to do this question.

> Enter 9 on your calculator.
> Add 10 and keep on adding 10.
>
> **(a)** What do you notice about the way the answers change?
> **(b)** Does it make any difference if you start by entering 19?

> Enter 9 on your calculator.
> Add 20 and keep adding 20.
>
> **(c)** What do you notice about the way the answers change?
> **(d)** Does it make any difference if you start by entering 19?

> Enter 9 on your calculator.
> Add 30 and keep on adding 30.
>
> **(e)** What do you notice about the way the answers change?
> **(f)** Does it make any difference if you start by entering 19?

Do the rest of this exercise mentally.
Do not use a calculator.

2 (a) $26 + 10$ (b) $45 + 10$ (c) $32 - 10$
   (d) $54 - 10$ (e) $87 + 10$ (f) $94 - 10$
   (g) $24 + 20$ (h) $47 + 20$ (i) $54 + 20$
   (j) $35 - 20$ (k) $82 - 20$ (l) $77 - 20$
   (m) $16 + 30$ (n) $32 + 30$ (o) $74 - 30$
   (p) $46 - 30$ (q) $54 + 30$ (r) $94 - 30$

3 (a) $22 + 40$ (b) $34 + 50$ (c) $29 + 70$
   (d) $74 - 40$ (e) $86 - 50$ (f) $98 - 70$
   (g) $15 + 80$ (h) $68 - 50$ (i) $23 + 60$
   (j) $51 + 40$ (k) $79 - 50$ (l) $88 - 60$

4 (a) $14 + 10 + 20$ (b) $47 + 10 + 20$ (c) $33 + 30 + 20$
   (d) $42 + 30 + 10$ (e) $15 + 30 + 40$ (f) $27 + 40 + 20$
   (g) $18 + 40 + 30$ (h) $39 + 30 + 30$

5 (a) $95 - 10 - 20$ (b) $89 - 10 - 20$
   (c) $67 - 30 - 20$ (d) $76 - 30 - 10$
   (e) $56 - 20 - 30$ (f) $87 - 40 - 30$
   (g) $99 - 40 - 40$ (h) $91 - 50 - 40$

6 (a) $23 + 40 - 10$ (b) $35 + 60 - 20$
   (c) $64 - 30 + 20$ (d) $48 + 50 - 30$
   (e) $62 - 20 + 30$ (f) $41 + 40 - 60$
   (g) $64 - 40 + 10$ (h) $67 - 50 + 80$

7 Pick a number from each cloud and add
   them together.

   How many different answers can you
   make by doing this?

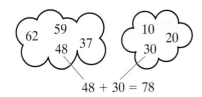

$48 + 30 = 78$

8 Pick a number from each cloud.

   Add the first two numbers then
   subtract the third number.

   How many different numbers can
   you make by doing this?

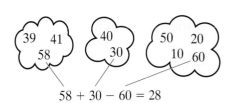

$58 + 30 - 60 = 28$

2.7 Mental maths methods

Here are some easy ways to do mental calculations by adding or subtracting 10:

Two ways to add 9 and 12

$$9 + 12 =$$

12 is 10 + 2

$$9 + 10 + 2$$

$$19 \quad + 2 = 21$$

So 9 + 12 = 21

$$12 + 9 =$$

9 is 10 − 1

$$12 + 10 - 1$$

$$22 \quad - 1 = 21$$

So 9 + 12 = 21

Two ways to subtract 11 from 19

$$19 - 11$$

11 is 10 + 1

To subtract 11, first subtract 10, then subtract 1.

$$19 - 10 - 1 = 8$$

So 19 − 11 = 8

$$19 - 11$$

11 is 10 + 1

To subtract 11, first subtract 1, then subtract 10.

$$19 - 1 - 10 = 8$$

So 19 − 11 = 8

To remember these methods just remember two examples:

- **To add 9, first add 10, then subtract 1**

- **To subtract 11, first subtract 10, then subtract 1**

Exercise 2G

Work these out mentally:

1 17 + 9	**2** 25 − 11	**3** 16 + 8	**4** 19 − 9
5 22 + 9	**6** 32 − 11	**7** 29 − 12	**8** 43 + 8

9 $51 - 9$ **10** $49 + 8$ **11** $27 + 9$ **12** $40 - 11$

13 $73 - 9$ **14** $26 + 8$ **15** $43 - 8$ **16** $17 - 8$

Copy and complete these sentences:

17 To add 8 you add 10 then take away ___ .

18 To take away 8 you take away ___ then add ___ .

19 To subtract 9 you subtract ___ then add ___ .

20 To subtract 12 you subtract ___ then subtract ___ .

2.8 Mental maths: adding two-digit numbers

■ **You can make adding easier by breaking up numbers.**

Here are two ways to add 31 and 27:

$31 + 27 =$
$31 + 20 + 7$
$51 \quad + 7 = 58$
So $31 + 27 = 58$

$31 + 27 =$
$31 + 7 + 20$
$38 \quad + 20 = 58$
So $31 + 27 = 58$

Exercise 2H

You should do this exercise mentally.
Do not use a calculator.

1   **(a)** $34 + 23$ **(b)** $25 + 23$ **(c)** $37 + 21$ **(d)** $31 + 25$ Hint: it might be
    (e) $46 + 33$ **(f)** $25 + 72$ **(g)** $32 + 55$ **(h)** $76 + 21$ easier to think of
    (i) $37 + 12$ **(j)** $24 + 73$ **(k)** $67 + 22$ **(l)** $26 + 51$ this as $72 + 25$.

2   **(a)** $38 + 24$ **(b)** $49 + 25$ **(c)** $48 + 36$ **(d)** $68 + 23$
    (e) $37 + 55$ **(f)** $28 + 43$ **(g)** $42 + 29$ **(h)** $37 + 23$
    (i) $54 + 36$ **(j)** $29 + 53$ **(k)** $44 + 28$ **(l)** $36 + 36$

3 **Activity** You need ten cards numbered:
0, 1, 2, 3, 4, 5, 6, 7, 8, 9.
Put them in a bag or box and pick out four cards.
Arrange the four cards to make two two-digit numbers.

Add them together.

Rearrange the cards to make two more
two-digit numbers and add them together.

$\boxed{5}\ \boxed{7}\ +\ \boxed{3}\ \boxed{2}\ =\ 89$

$\boxed{3}\ \boxed{7}\ +\ \boxed{2}\ \boxed{5}\ =\ 62$

(a) How many different pairs of two-digit
numbers can you make?

(b) How many different totals do you get?

(c) Which arrangement gives the biggest total?

(d) Which arrangement gives the smallest total?

Hint: try to find a
system for writing
down all the pairs of
2-digit numbers

4 Put the cards back in the bag and repeat question **3**.

5 **Activity** You need a 100 square.
Draw a rectangle on a 100 number square.
Add the numbers in opposite corners of the
rectangle like this:
Do this for other rectangles.
What do you notice?
Explain any pattern you notice.

$12 + 35$

1	2	3	4	5	6	7	8	9	10
11	12	13	14	15	16	17	18	19	20
21	22	23	24	25	26	27	28	29	30
31	32	33	34	35	36	37	38	39	40
41	42	43	44	45	46	47	48	49	50

$32 + 15$

2.9 Mental maths: subtracting two-digit numbers

■ **You can make subtracting easier by breaking up
numbers.**

Here are two ways to subtract 28 from 65:

$65 - 28$

$65 - 20 - 8$

$45 \quad - 8 = 37$

So $65 - 28 = 37$

$65 - 28$

$65 - 8 - 20$

$57 \quad - 20 = 37$

So $65 - 28 = 37$

Exercise 2I

Do this exercise mentally. Do not use a calculator.

1 (a) $34 - 13$ (b) $45 - 12$ (c) $37 - 14$ (d) $68 - 24$
  (e) $53 - 21$ (f) $78 - 25$ (g) $64 - 31$ (h) $86 - 42$
  (i) $96 - 52$ (j) $89 - 63$ (k) $48 - 31$ (l) $93 - 71$

2 (a) $34 - 15$ (b) $43 - 24$ (c) $36 - 17$ (d) $54 - 26$
  (e) $44 - 18$ (f) $67 - 39$ (g) $56 - 28$ (h) $63 - 35$
  (i) $84 - 57$ (j) $93 - 47$ (k) $75 - 27$ (l) $88 - 59$

3 These pupils have each chosen a pair of two-digit numbers from the whiteboard.

Remember: the difference means the largest number take away the smallest number. The difference between 28 and 53 is $53 - 28 = 25$

Lauren — The difference between my pair is 9

Nadia — The difference for my pair is 36

Ahmed — The difference for my pair is 25

Wayne — The difference for my pair is 38

WHAT'S MY PAIR OF NUMBERS?

34   46
        74   38
25   56   63

Which pair of numbers has each pupil chosen?

4 **Activity**

Choose any four two-digit numbers and write them at the four corners of a square.

```
43 ——— 27
|         |
|         |
16 ——— 83
```

Work out the difference between the numbers on each edge of the square and write the difference at the middle of that edge.

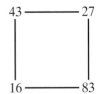

```
43 — 16 — 27
|   /   \   |
27         57
|   \   /   |
16 — 68 — 84
```

Join the four new numbers to make a square.

Work out the difference between the numbers at the ends of each edge of the new square and write the difference at the middle of that edge

```
43 — 16 — 27
|  11 — 41  |
27         57
|  41 — 11  |
16 — 68 — 84
```

Join the four new numbers to make a square.

  (a) Continue this process until it is obvious you should stop.
  (b) Repeat (a) using another four two-digit numbers.
  (c) Explain what is happening.

(d) Try choosing three two-digit numbers and writing them at the corners of a triangle.

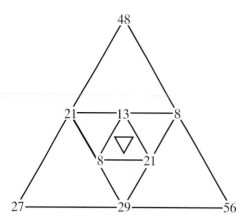

5 Start with 100.

Move along the arrows from start to finish, subtracting the numbers shown on the arrows as you go.

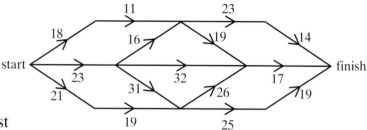

(a) What is the smallest number you can finish with?

(b) What is the largest number you can finish with?

2.10 Using mental maths to solve problems

You can use mental maths to solve everyday problems.

First decide whether to add or subtract to solve the problem.

These words usually mean you **add**:

total, sum, altogether, plus

These words and phrases usually mean you **subtract**:

minus, take away, less
How many more?
How much change?
What is the difference between…?

Example 4

Paul bought a bar of chocolate for 38p and a packet of chewing gum for 45p.

How much change did he get from a £1 coin?

The total cost was $38 + 45 = 83$p

The change was $£1 - 83p = 100p - 83p = 17p.$

Exercise 2J

1 In a class of children there are 17 girls and 15 boys.

What is the total number of children in the class?

> **Class 7B**
> Girls 17
> Boys 15
> Total ...

2 Two classes of children went on a trip together. There were 34 children from one class and 29 children from the other class.
How many children went on the trip?

3 98 children from a school went on a half day visit.
47 children went in the morning.
How many went in the afternoon?

4 A water tank holds 72 litres when full.
There are 44 litres of water in the tank.
How many more litres of water can be put into the tank?

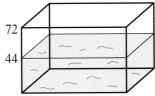

5 Zoe buys a drink for 48p and a bar of chocolate for 36p.

(a) What is the total cost?

(b) What change should she get if she pays with a £1 coin?

6 An electricity pylon is 33 metres tall.
A church tower is 25 metres tall.
How much taller is the pylon than the tower?

7 In a pond there are 28 mirror carp and 65 koi carp.

  (a) What is the total number of carp in the pond?

  (b) How many more koi carp than mirror carp are there?

8 In a class of 32 children, 18 have school dinner and the rest bring packed lunches.
How many children bring packed lunches?

> **Class 8C**
> School dinner   18
> Packed lunches . . .
> Total   32

9 In a darts match Morag scored 54 and 18 with her first two darts. After her third dart she had scored a total of 96.
What did she score with her third dart?

10 A computer shop had software for sale at these prices.
Marco bought three items of software for a total cost of £90.
Find all the possible costs of the three items Marco bought.

£18   £40   £44

£32   £6   £52

£28

£20   £30

2.11 Adding numbers on paper

You can add large numbers together on paper.
Sometimes it's easier than adding them in your head.

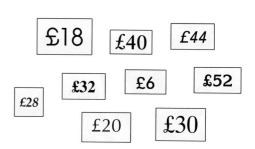

Line up the units. Use headings to help you.	Add the units together. $4 + 5 = 9$	Now add the tens. $2 + 6 = 8$	Add the hundreds. $1 + 3 = 4$
H T U 1 2 4 +3 6 5 ___	H T U 1 2 4 +3 6 5 ___ 9	H T U 1 2 4 +3 6 5 __ 8 9	H T U 1 2 4 +3 6 5 4 8 9

Example 5

Add 35 and 48.

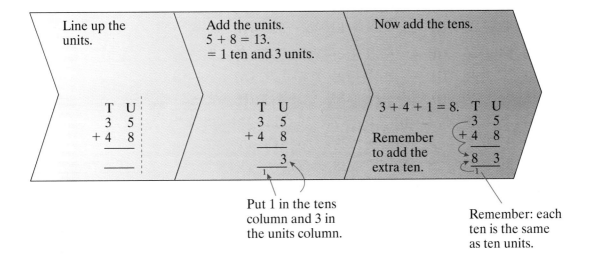

So   35 + 48 = 83

You can check your answer on a number line.

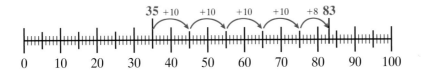

Example 6

Add 28, 17 and 36.

Add the units:	Now add the tens:

```
     T U
     2 8
     1 7
   + 3 6
   ──────
       1   ←── Put 1 in the units column
     2 ←──── and 2 in the tens column
```

8 + 7 + 6 = 21
  = 2 tens and 1 unit

```
           T U
           2 8
           1 7
         + 3 6
         ──────
           8 1
           2
```

2 + 1 + 3 + 2 = 8

Remember to add
the extra 2 tens

Exercise 2K

1. (a) $38 + 25$ (b) $46 + 18$ (c) $52 + 36$ (d) $35 + 23$
    (e) $49 + 28$ (f) $33 + 28$ (g) $73 + 24$ (h) $64 + 29$
    (i) $43 + 27$ (j) $62 + 28$ (k) $46 + 46$ (l) $69 + 29$

2. (a) $54 + 23$ (b) $45 + 38$ (c) $56 + 39$ (d) $27 + 54$
    (e) $32 + 49$ (f) $43 + 27$ (g) $26 + 67$ (h) $38 + 48$
    (i) $38 + 38$ (j) $22 + 47$ (k) $37 + 27$ (l) $59 + 24$

3. (a) $35 + 26 + 23$ (b) $34 + 37 + 25$ (c) $27 + 34 + 28$
    (d) $37 + 29 + 28$ (e) $29 + 28 + 36$ (f) $46 + 28 + 16$
    (g) $39 + 25 + 28$ (h) $17 + 28 + 37$

4. (a) $85 + 54$ (b) $76 + 49$ (c) $64 + 83$ (d) $91 + 38$
    (e) $87 + 68$ (f) $55 + 79$ (g) $89 + 89$ (h) $67 + 75$
    (i) $73 + 67$ (j) $48 + 52$ (k) $86 + 95$ (l) $56 + 49$

5. (a) $46 + 43 + 34$ (b) $53 + 65 + 34$ (c) $36 + 81 + 57$
    (d) $48 + 37 + 39$ (e) $28 + 69 + 36$ (f) $73 + 80 + 84$
    (g) $89 + 86 + 78$ (h) $88 + 94 + 79$

6. (a) $259 + 134$ (b) $407 + 285$ (c) $658 + 183$
    (d) $758 + 681$ (e) $679 + 583$ (f) $398 + 843$
    (g) $564 + 487$ (h) $672 + 428$ (i) $837 + 163$
    (j) $987 + 689$

7. (a) $642 + 25$ (b) $368 + 24$ (c) $49 + 374$
    (d) $465 + 78$ (e) $67 + 206$ (f) $535 + 85$
    (g) $724 + 79$ (h) $563 + 37$ (i) $59 + 684$
    (j) $96 + 748$

Remember to line up the units first.

8. You can use the digits 2, 3, 4 and 5 to make a pair of two-digit numbers that add up to 77.
    Using the same digits find other pairs of two-digit numbers that add up to 77.

$$\begin{array}{r} 45 \\ + 32 \\ \hline 77 \end{array}$$

9. Using only the digits 3, 4, 5 and 6 find pairs of two-digit numbers that add up to 99.

10. Pick a pair of numbers from this cloud and add them together.

    (a) What is the largest answer you can get?
    (b) What is the smallest answer you can get?
    (c) Which pair of numbers gives an answer closest to 100?

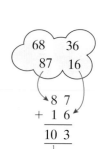

11 Repeat question **10** for each of these clouds.

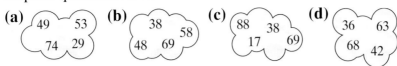

(a) 49 53 74 29   **(b)** 38 48 69 58   **(c)** 88 38 17 69   **(d)** 36 63 68 42

12 Find the digits to fill each box, ☐, in these addition sums.

(a)
```
   5 ☐
 + ☐ 5
 ─────
   7 8
```

(b)
```
   3 ☐
 + ☐ 2
 ─────
   8 8
```

(c)
```
   4 ☐
 + ☐ 7
 ─────
   8 2
```

(d)
```
   2 ☐
 + ☐ 4
 ─────
   6 3
```

(e)
```
   8 ☐
 + ☐ 2
 ─────
   9 6
```

(f)
```
   2 1
   4 ☐
 + ☐ 7
 ─────
   9 6
```

(g)
```
   ☐ 7
   3 ☐
 + 1 8
 ─────
   8 1
```

(h)
```
   2 6
   1 ☐
 + ☐ 8
 ─────
   9 3
```

(i)
```
   3 ☐
   ☐ 7
 + 1 9
 ─────
   8 4
```

(j)
```
   1 ☐
   3 5
 + ☐ 4
 ─────
   9 5
```

(k)
```
   3 ☐
   ☐ 2
 + 6 3
 ─────
 1 7 9
```

(l)
```
   ☐ 8
   6 3
 + 2 ☐
 ─────
 1 3 7
```

(m)
```
   9 ☐
   7 2
 + ☐ 5
 ─────
 2 5 3
```

(n)
```
   ☐ 9
   8 ☐
 + 3 5
 ─────
 ☐ 7 1
```

(o)
```
   8 6
   4 ☐
 + ☐ 8
 ─────
 ☐ 1 3
```

13 Choose any three-digit number.
Reverse the digits.
Add the two numbers together.

```
   528
 + 825
 ─────
  1353
  1 1
```

Reverse the digits of the answer.
Add the two numbers.

```
  1353
 +3531
 ─────
  4884
```

4884 is called a palindromic number.
A palindromic number stays the same when you reverse its digits.

Try this for each of these three-digit numbers.

(a) 427   **(b)** 635   **(c)** 834   **(d)** 264 ──

Keep reversing the digits and adding until you get a palindromic number.

(e) Try other three-digit numbers.

Do you always get a palindromic number eventually?

2.12 Subtracting numbers on paper

You can subtract two numbers on paper like this:

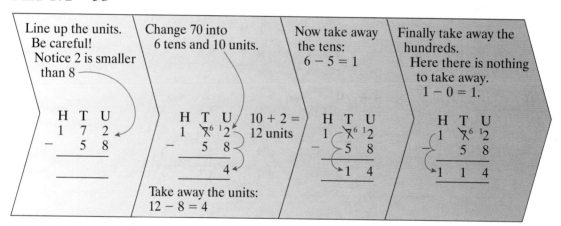

To find 289 − 153 first line up the units:

```
  H  T  U
   2  8  9
-  1  5  3
  _____
```

Subtract the units: 9 − 3 = 6

```
  H  T  U
   2  8  9
-  1  5  3
  _____
         6
```

Subtract the tens: 8 − 5 = 3

```
  H  T  U
   2  8  9
-  1  5  3
  _____
      3  6
```

Subtract the hundreds: 2 − 1 = 1

```
  H  T  U
   2  8  9
-  1  5  3
  _____
   1  3  6
```

Example 7

Find 172 − 58

Line up the units. Be careful! Notice 2 is smaller than 8

```
  H  T  U
   1  7  2
-     5  8
  _____
```

Change 70 into 6 tens and 10 units.

```
  H  T  U
   1  ⁶7̸ ¹2
-     5  8
  _____
         4
```
10 + 2 = 12 units

Take away the units: 12 − 8 = 4

Now take away the tens: 6 − 5 = 1

```
  H  T  U
   1  ⁶7̸ ¹2
-     5  8
  _____
      1  4
```

Finally take away the hundreds. Here there is nothing to take away. 1 − 0 = 1.

```
  H  T  U
   1  ⁶7̸ ¹2
-     5  8
  _____
   1  1  4
```

Exercise 2L

1
(a) 85 − 23   (b) 54 − 31   (c) 67 − 46   (d) 38 − 23
(e) 96 − 21   (f) 47 − 37   (g) 59 − 54   (h) 78 − 48
(i) 96 − 14   (j) 77 − 25   (k) 48 − 36   (l) 59 − 23

2
(a) 64 − 27   (b) 43 − 29   (c) 56 − 27   (d) 36 − 19
(e) 80 − 47   (f) 61 − 28   (g) 53 − 45   (h) 90 − 38
(i) 57 − 38   (j) 70 − 28   (k) 48 − 19   (l) 91 − 25

3
(a) 687 − 543   (b) 496 − 132   (c) 584 − 230
(d) 769 − 345   (e) 947 − 207   (f) 856 − 653
(g) 478 − 278   (h) 574 − 532   (i) 769 − 719
(j) 685 − 681   (k) 357 − 351   (l) 113 − 101

4   **(a)** 546 − 127   **(b)** 864 − 328   **(c)** 750 − 416
        (d) 457 − 208   **(e)** 675 − 467   **(f)** 947 − 362
        (g) 854 − 671   **(h)** 605 − 294   **(i)** 748 − 656
        (j) 537 − 492   **(k)** 537 − 238   **(l)** 852 − 357
        (m) 645 − 269   **(n)** 543 − 465   **(o)** 767 − 689

5   **(a)** 684 − 23   **(b)** 567 − 32   **(c)** 483 − 53
        (d) 494 − 60   **(e)** 539 − 31   **(f)** 486 − 28
        (g) 563 − 37   **(h)** 743 − 38   **(i)** 646 − 62
        (j) 534 − 71   **(k)** 845 − 75   **(l)** 736 − 62
        (m) 428 − 59   **(n)** 942 − 78   **(o)** 356 − 89

6   Pick a pair of numbers, one from each cloud, and find the difference.

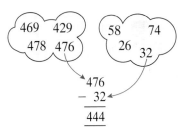

   (a) Which pair gives the largest answer?

   (b) Which pair gives the smallest answer?

   (c) Which pair gives the answer closest to 400?

7   Repeat question **6** for this pair of clouds.

8   Put the digits 4, 5, 6, 7 and 8 in the boxes of this take-away sum and work out the answer.

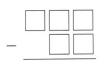

   (a) Which arrangement gives the biggest answer?

   (b) Which arrangement gives the smallest answer?

   (c) Which arrangement gives the answer closest to 500?

9   Take any two-digit number   36
        Reverse the digits to make another two-digit number.   63

Find the difference of the two numbers.

$$\begin{array}{r} 63 \\ -36 \\ \hline 27 \end{array}$$

Do the same for the answer,

$$\begin{array}{r} {}^{6}\!\!\not{7}{}^{1}2 \\ -27 \\ \hline 45 \end{array}$$

and again.

$$\begin{array}{r} {}^{4}\!\!\not{5}{}^{1}4 \\ -45 \\ \hline 9 \end{array}$$

Try this for other two-digit numbers.
Do you always get the answer 9 eventually?
Does the same happen for three-digit numbers?

Summary of key points

1   The value of a digit depends on its place in a
        number.
        You can see this in a place value diagram:

The digit 4
means ...

	Hundreds	Tens	Units	
4 hundreds	4	7	9	Four hundred and seventy nine
4 tens	2	4	3	Two hundred and forty three
4 units	7	0	4	Seven hundred and four

2   82 is a two-digit number because it has two digits
        704 is a three-digit number because it has three
        digits

        704 is also called a three-figure number.

3 When you add 10 the units digit stays the same:

$$8 + 10 = 18 \qquad \text{or} \qquad \begin{array}{r} 10 \\ 8 + \\ \hline 18 \end{array}$$

When you subtract 10 from a larger number the units digit stays the same:

$$37 - 10 = 27 \qquad \text{or} \qquad \begin{array}{r} 37 \\ 10 - \\ \hline 27 \end{array}$$

4 To add 9, first add 10, then subtract 1

To subtract 11, first subtract 10, then subtract 1

5 You can make adding easier by breaking up numbers.

6 You can make subtracting easier by breaking up numbers.

3 Number patterns

People have been fascinated by number patterns for centuries.

You will explore some number patterns in this unit.

This altar in China has nine circles, each with a multiple of nine stones.
The ancient Chinese believed that using nine's brought them closer to Heaven.

3.1 Patterns from matchsticks

Here are the first four shapes in a matchstick pattern:

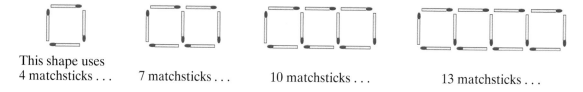

This shape uses
4 matchsticks . . .   7 matchsticks . . .   10 matchsticks . . .   13 matchsticks . . .

Using numbers the pattern is:

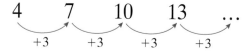

4   7   10   13   . . .
  +3   +3   +3   +3

The rule to go from one shape to the next is '**add 3**'.

Exercise 3A

Copy these matchstick patterns.
For each pattern:

- draw the next two shapes
- write down the pattern using numbers
- write down the rule to go from one shape to the next.

1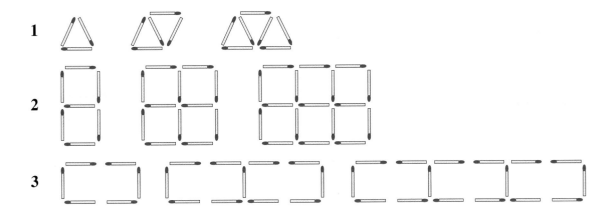

2

3

3.2 Dot patterns

Here are the first five shapes in a dot pattern:

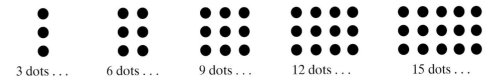

3 dots . . . 6 dots . . . 9 dots . . . 12 dots . . . 15 dots . . .

Using numbers the pattern is:

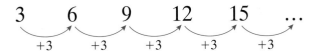

3   6   9   12   15   ...
  +3   +3   +3   +3   +3

The rule to go from one shape to the next is '**add 3**'.

Exercise 3B

1 Copy the dot patterns below.
For each pattern:

- write down the pattern using numbers
- write down the rule to go from one shape to the next.

(a)

(b)

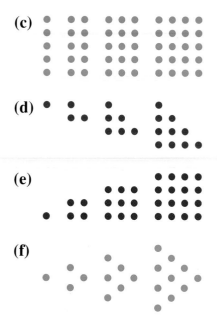

(c)

(d)

(e)

(f)

2 Draw dots to show these number patterns.
Write down what you notice about them.

(a) 2, 4, 6, 8, 10
(b) 0, 5, 10, 15, 20
(c) 2, 5, 8, 11, 14
(d) 3, 7, 11, 15, 19
(e) 1, 7, 13, 19, 25

3.3 Number machines

■ **You can use number machines to make number patterns.**

Here is a number machine for multiplying by 3:

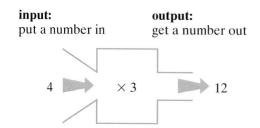

input:
put a number in

output:
get a number out

4   × 3   12

If you put a number pattern into a number machine, the
output numbers will make a pattern too.

Example 1

(a) Input the number pattern 1, 2, 3, 4, 5, and 6 into this machine:

(b) List the output numbers.

(c) Describe the pattern.

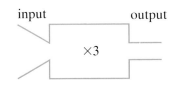

(a)

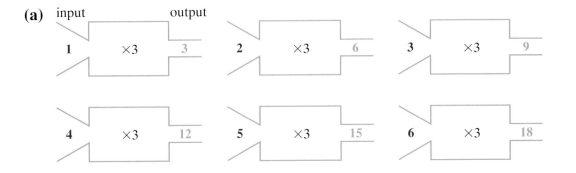

or:

Write your results in a table like this:

input	output
1 ×3	3
2 ×3	6
3 ×3	9
4 ×3	12
5 ×3	15
6 ×3	18

×3

Notice that you can see the pattern if you shade the output numbers on a 100 square. The pattern continues...

(b) The output numbers are 3, 6, 9, 12, 15 and 18.

(c) The pattern is: the output numbers go up in 3's.

1	2	3	4	5	6	7	8	9	10
11	12	13	14	15	16	17	18	19	20
21	22	23	24	25	26	27	28	29	30
31	32	33	34	35	36	37	38	39	40
41	42	43	44	45	46	47	48	49	50
51	52	53	54	55	56	57	58	59	60
61	62	63	64	65	66	67	68	69	70
71	72	73	74	75	76	77	78	79	80
81	82	83	84	85	86	87	88	89	90
91	92	93	94	95	96	97	98	99	100

Exercise 3C

For each question:

(a) Input the number pattern 1, 2, 3, 4, 5, 6.

(b) List the output numbers.

(c) Describe the pattern.

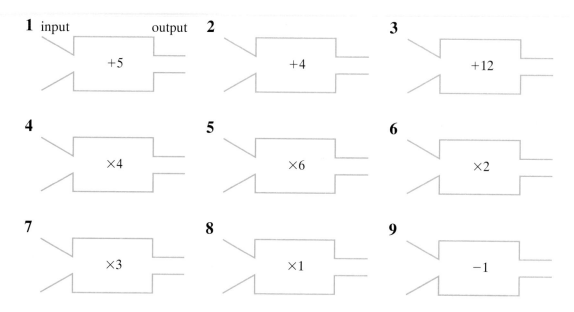

1 input   output   +5

2   +4

3   +12

4   ×4

5   ×6

6   ×2

7   ×3

8   ×1

9   −1

3.4 Sequences

Another name for a number pattern is a **sequence**.

■ **A sequence is a number pattern.**
The numbers are usually written in a row like this:

2, 4, 6, 8, 10, ...

The dots show the sequence goes on forever.

Example 2

(a) Describe this sequence of numbers in words.
(b) Find the next two numbers in the sequence.

1, 4, 7, 10, 13, 16, ...

(a) The numbers go up in threes. So the sequence is:
Start at 1 and keep adding on 3.

(b) To find the next two numbers you add on three

$$16 + 3 = 19$$
$$19 + 3 = 22$$

The next two numbers are 19 and 22.

Example 3

(a) Find the next number in the sequence:

12, 10, 8, 6, 4, ...

(b) Write down the rule for finding the next number.

(a) The numbers go down by 2 each time, so you take away 2 to find the next number:

$$4 - 2 = 2.$$

The next number is 2.

(b) The rule is: take away 2.

Exercise 3D

For each sequence:

(a) Write down the next two numbers.

(b) Write down the rule for finding the next number.

1 1, 3, 5, 7, 9, ..., ...   **2** 0, 3, 6, 9, 12, ..., ...

3 0, 5, 10, 15, ..., ...   **4** 2, 5, 8, 11, 14, ..., ...

5 1, 2, 3, 4, 5, ..., ...   **6** 1, 4, 7, 10, 13, ..., ...

7 4, 8, 12, 16, 20, ..., ...   **8** 10, 20, 30, 40, ..., ...

9 3, 7, 11, 15, 19, ..., ...   **10** 2, 6, 10, 14, ..., ...

11 0, 7, 14, 21, 28, ..., ...   **12** 9, 18, 27, 36, ..., ...

13 20, 18, 16, 14, 12, ..., ...   **14** 18, 15, 12, 9, ..., ...

15 25, 10, 15, 10, ..., ...   **16** 19, 17, 15, 13, ..., ...

17 70, 60, 50, 40, ..., ...   **18** 20, 17, 14, 11, ..., ...

19 8, 7, 6, 5, 4, ..., ...   **20** 23, 19, 15, 11, ..., ...

21 16, 13, 10, 7, ..., ...   **22** 23, 21, 19, 17, ..., ...

23 80, 75, 70, 65, ..., ...   **24** 54, 45, 36, 27, ..., ...

Example 4

Find the missing numbers in these sequences:

(a) 32, 28, 24, __, __, 12, __

(b) 3, 6, 12, __, __, 96

(a)

The rule connecting the numbers is **subtract 4**.

(b)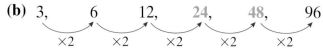

The rule connecting the numbers is **multiply by 2**.

Exercise 3E

Find the missing numbers in these sequences:

1 1, 3, 9, __, __, 243, __

2 64, 59, 54, __, __, 39, __

3 108, 96, 84, __, __, 48, __

4 7, 14, 21, __, __, 42, __, 56

5 0, 10, 20, __, __, 50, __

6 38, 34, 30, __, __, 18, __

7 1, 2, 4, __, __, 32

8 90, 80, 70, __, __, 40, __

9 3, 7, 11, __, __, 23, __, __

3.5 Two step number machines

This is a two step number machine.

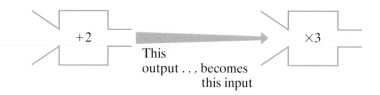

This
output . . . becomes
        this input

Example 5

For this two step number machine,
find the output if the input is 5.

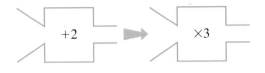

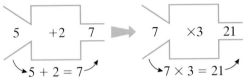

The output is 21.

You can also make patterns with two step machines.

Example 6

(a) Input the number pattern 1, 2, 3, 4 and 5
in this machine.
(b) Show your results in a table.
(c) Describe the pattern of output numbers.

(a)

input 1: 1 ×2 2 ➡ 2 −1 1
1 × 2 = 2   2 − 1 = 1

input 2: 2 ×2 4 ➡ 4 −1 3
2 × 2 = 4   4 − 1 = 3

input 3:   3 × 2 = 6 ➡ 6 − 1 = 5
input 4:   4 × 2 = 8 ➡ 8 − 1 = 7
input 5:   5 × 2 = 10 ➡ 10 − 1 = 9

(b)

×2 ➤ −1

input	output
1	1
2	3
3	5
4	7
5	9

(c) The pattern is: the output numbers go up in 2's.
The output numbers are the odd numbers.

■ **In a two step number machine the output from the first
machine becomes the input for the second machine.**

Exercise 3F

Write down the output numbers for these two step machines.

1 $\boxed{3 \quad \times 2} \quad \boxed{+3}$ 2 $\boxed{5 \quad \times 3} \quad \boxed{+1}$

3 $\boxed{2 \quad \times 4} \quad \boxed{+3}$ 4 $\boxed{4 \quad \times 3} \quad \boxed{-2}$

5 $\boxed{3 \quad \times 5} \quad \boxed{-4}$ 6 $\boxed{5 \quad \times 10} \quad \boxed{+2}$

7 $\boxed{6 \quad \times 5} \quad \boxed{-10}$ 8 $\boxed{2 \quad \times 6} \quad \boxed{-12}$

For questions **9** to **17**:

(a) Input the numbers 1, 2, 3, 4, 5, 6.

(b) Show your results in a table.

(c) Describe the pattern of output numbers.

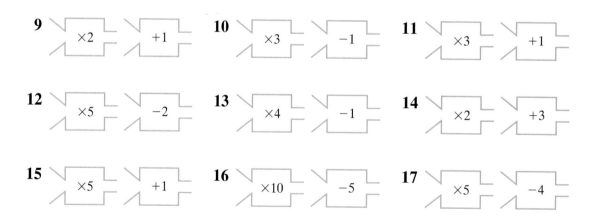

9 $\boxed{\times 2} \quad \boxed{+1}$ 10 $\boxed{\times 3} \quad \boxed{-1}$ 11 $\boxed{\times 3} \quad \boxed{+1}$

12 $\boxed{\times 5} \quad \boxed{-2}$ 13 $\boxed{\times 4} \quad \boxed{-1}$ 14 $\boxed{\times 2} \quad \boxed{+3}$

15 $\boxed{\times 5} \quad \boxed{+1}$ 16 $\boxed{\times 10} \quad \boxed{-5}$ 17 $\boxed{\times 5} \quad \boxed{-4}$

18 Use the numbers 2, 3, 5, 7, 11 in the two step machines in questions **9** to **14**. Show your results in a table.

3.6 Some special number patterns

Here are three number patterns you need to be able to recognize:

Square numbers

This dot pattern shows some **square numbers**:

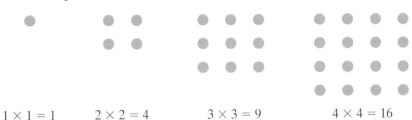

$1 \times 1 = 1$ $2 \times 2 = 4$ $3 \times 3 = 9$ $4 \times 4 = 16$

> You can see how to use your calculator for square numbers on page 232.

■ **A square number is the result of multiplying a number by itself.**

Triangular numbers

This dot pattern shows some **triangular numbers**:

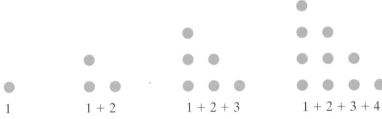

1   1 + 2   1 + 2 + 3   1 + 2 + 3 + 4

Fibonacci sequences

These numbers form a **Fibonacci sequence**:

   1, 1, 2, 3, 5, 8, 13 ...

Here is how to make the sequence:

The sizes of the diamonds on this pineapple's surface are linked by the Fibonacci sequence.

These two numbers start the sequence.

1 1 2 3 5 8 13 . . .   1 1 2 3 5 8 13 . . .

Add the first two numbers . . .

Add the next two numbers . . .   . . . and so on

Exercise 3G

1 From this list of numbers:

9, 6, 8, 1, 3, 13, 2

write down:
(a) the square numbers
(b) the triangular numbers
(c) the Fibonacci numbers

2 Write down:
(a) the fourth square number
(b) the fifth Fibonacci number
(c) the sixth square number
(d) the seventh triangular number
(e) the eighth Fibonacci number

Summary of key points

1 You can use number machines to make number
patterns.
Here is a number machine for multiplying by 3:

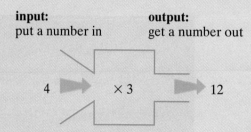

input:
put a number in

output:
get a number out

4   × 3   12

2 A sequence is a number pattern.
The numbers are usually written in a row like this:

2, 4, 6, 8, 10, . . .

The dots show the sequence goes
on forever.

3   In a two step number machine the output from the first machine becomes the input for the second machine:

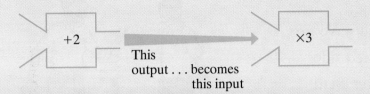

This
output ... becomes
this input

4   A square number is the result of multiplying a number by itself.
For example:

$$1 \times 1 = 1 \qquad 2 \times 2 = 4 \qquad 3 \times 3 = 9 \qquad 10 \times 10 = 100$$

square numbers

5   Here is how to make a sequence of triangular numbers:

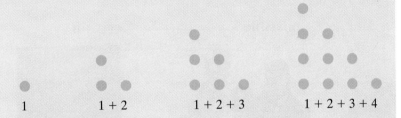

1   1 + 2   1 + 2 + 3   1 + 2 + 3 + 4

6   Here is how to make a Fibonacci sequence:

1 1 2 3 5 8 13 ...

Add the first
two numbers ...

1 1 2 3 5 8 13 ...

Then add the
next two numbers ...   ... and so on.

4 Probability

Philip and Sarah are going to play tennis. Sarah spins her raquet to decide who will serve first.

It has a blue side and a red side.

Spinning the racquet is an **event**.

This event has two possible outcomes: blue and red.

In this unit you will learn how to measure the chance of different outcomes happening.

4.1 Certain, impossible or possible

The outcome of an event may be:

impossible

You will get 12 out of 10 in a Geography test.

possible

It will rain tomorrow.

certain

The sun will rise tomorrow.

Example 1

Write down whether these outcomes are: impossible, possible or certain

(a) A car will break down on the M25 tomorrow.
(b) A dog will have kittens.
(c) Tuesday will be the day after Monday next week.

(a) It is possible that a car will break down on the M25 tomorrow.

(b) It is impossible for a dog to have kittens.

(c) It is certain that Tuesday will be the day after Monday next week.

It is not certain or impossible.

Exercise 4A

Write down whether these outcomes are:
certain, impossible or possible.

1　The school netball team will win their next match.

2　You will throw a 7 with a normal dice.

3　A red car will pass the school this evening.

4　You will have chips for tea tonight.

5　Thursday will be the day after Wednesday next week.

6　A plane will land at Manchester airport tomorrow.

7　Your friend will go to the moon next summer.

8　A cat will have puppies next year.

9　You will have a birthday next year.

10　You will receive a telephone call from a friend tonight.

4.2 Likely or unlikely?

Some outcomes are more likely to happen than others:

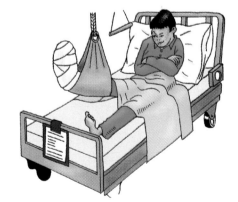

It is likely that you will eat breakfast tomorrow   It is unlikely that you will break a leg tomorrow

Example 2

Is this outcome likely or unlikely?
It will snow in Switzerland in
January.
Give a reason for your answer.

It is likely to snow in Switzerland
in January because Switzerland
has very cold winters.

Exercise 4B

Is each outcome likely or unlikely?
Give a reason for your answer.

1 You will break your leg next week.

2 You will see a famous film star in school next week.

3 You will watch Eastenders tonight.

4 Someone in your class will be absent next week.

5 It will rain in England in April.

6 When a card is taken from a normal pack it will be a number card.

7 Copy the table. Complete it by filling in 5 likely and 5 unlikely outcomes.

Outcome	
Likely	Unlikely

4.3 An even chance

At the start of a football match a coin is tossed to decide which team kicks off.

There are two possible outcomes: heads or tails.

Both outcomes are equally likely.

Each outcome has an **even chance** of happening.

■ **When an event has two equally likely outcomes, each outcome has an even chance of happening.**

Exercise 4C

Which of these outcomes have an even chance of happening? Give a reason for each outcome you choose.

1 The next baby to be born will be female.

2 The next car to pass your school will be white.

3 You will have an accident on the way home.

4 The number on the top of an ordinary dice will be odd.

5 The top card in a well shuffled pack will be black.

4.4 How likely is it?

The outcomes of an event can have different chances of happening. This table shows the different chances:

Likelihood	Explanation
Impossible	There is no chance it will happen
Unlikely	It has a greater chance of not happening than happening
Even chance	It has the same chance of happening as not happening
Likely	It has a greater chance of happening than not happening
Certain	It will definitely happen

Example 3

Choose the likelihood which matches the outcome of each event:
impossible, unlikely, even chance, likely or certain.

Give a reason for your answers.

(a) The mountaineer will be hurt if he falls off the mountain.
(b) The number on the top face of an ordinary dice will be less than 7.
(c) Mr Smith will cut the grass on his lawn when it is snowing.
(d) The *Titanic* will float back up to the top of the ocean.
(e) The card at the top of a shuffled pack is a King.
(f) The card at the top of a shuffled pack is red.

(a) is likely. The mountain is hard and it will hurt if the mountaineer falls.
(b) is certain. The numbers on an ordinary dice are 1, 2, 3, 4, 5 and 6.
(c) is unlikely. Nobody with any sense cuts the grass when it is snowing.
(d) is impossible. The *Titanic* is made of metal and it will not rise.
(e) is unlikely. There are only 4 Kings in a pack of 52 cards.
(f) is an even chance. The top card will be either red or black.

Exercise 4D

Choose the likelihood which matches the outcome of each event: impossible, unlikely, an even chance, likely or certain.

Give a reason for your answers.

1 It will rain in London at some time during April.

2 The winner of next year's mens finals at Wimbledon will be aged over 30 years.

3 Next year's FA Cup Final will be won by a team from the third division.

4 The next baby to be born will be male.

5 There will be more hours of light during the night than during the day.

6 The record at number 1 in the charts this week will be in the top 10 next week.

7 The Division 1 title will be won by a team from Division 2.

8 Elvis Presley is still alive.

9 You will be involved in a road accident on your way home today.

10 Someone will be involved in a road accident today.

4.5 The likelihood scale

You can mark the chance of an outcome happening on a likelihood scale:

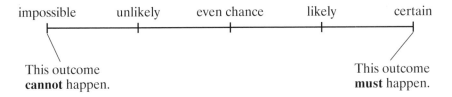

This outcome **cannot** happen.

This outcome **must** happen.

Example 4

Draw a likelihood scale.
Put each of these outcomes in a suitable place on your scale:

(a) It will rain in Ireland next year.

(b) The next baby to be born will be male.

(c) Your dog will live forever.

(d) The next car to pass your school will be P registered.

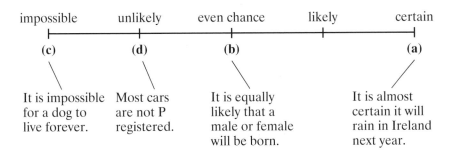

It is impossible for a dog to live forever.

Most cars are not P registered.

It is equally likely that a male or female will be born.

It is almost certain it will rain in Ireland next year.

■ **A likelihood scale runs from impossible to certain, with an 'even chance' in the middle.**

Exercise 4E

Draw a likelihood scale.
Mark an estimate of each of these outcomes on your scale.

(a) Sumreen's Budgie will live for ever.

(b) A car travelling on a motorway will be doing 25 miles per hour.

(c) The number on the top face of an ordinary dice will be even.

(d) The day after Christmas Day will be Boxing Day.

(e) It will rain in Manchester during at least one day in March next year.

4.6 Probability

■ **Probability uses numbers to measure the chance of an outcome happening.**

Probability was developed in the 17th Century when Mathematicians tried to work out the likelihood of success and failure in games of chance such as playing with cards or dice.

The probability scale

You can mark the probability of an outcome happening on a probability scale:

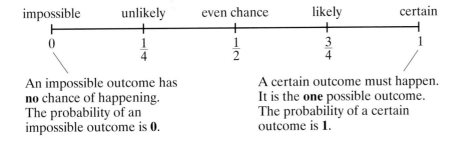

An impossible outcome has **no** chance of happening. The probability of an impossible outcome is **0**.

A certain outcome must happen. It is the **one** possible outcome. The probability of a certain outcome is **1**.

■ **All probabilities have a value from 0 to 1.**

Example 5

Mark each of these outcomes on a probability scale.
Give reasons for your answers.

(a) It will rain in Scotland on at least one day next year.
(b) The next object you see flying in the sky will be a pink elephant.
(c) The card on the top of a well shuffled pack will be red.
(d) It will be warm in London next July.
(e) The winner of next year's mens final at Wimbledon will be aged over 30.

(a) is certain, it is bound to rain at some time.
(b) is impossible.
(c) is an even chance, the card will be either red or black and both are equally likely.
(d) is likely.
(e) is unlikely, the winner is usually in his twenties.

So on the probability scale the answers look like this:

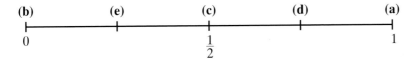

Exercise 4F

1 Draw a probability scale.
   Mark each of these outcomes on your scale.
   Give reasons for your answers.

   (a) The school bus will break down tomorrow.

   (b) The next baby to be born will be a girl.

   (c) An ice cube will melt when it is left outside on a hot day.

   (d) A heavy stone will float when it is dropped in the sea.

   (e) The winner of the women's Olympic 100 metres final will be aged under 35 years.

2 An ordinary pack of 52 cards is well shuffled.
   The top card is then turned over.
   Draw a probability scale and mark on it each of these outcomes:

   Give reasons for your answers

   (a) The top card will be black.

   (b) The top card will not be a picture card.

   (c) The top card will be a King.

   (d) The top card will be the Queen of Hearts.

   (e) The top card will be blank.

   (f) The top card will be either a number card or a picture card.

3 Look at this probability scale:

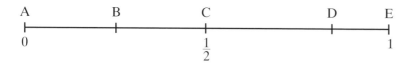

   Outcomes A, B, C, D and E have been marked on the scale.
   Give at least two possible outcomes for each of these probabilities.

Summary of key points

1   When an event has two equally likely outcomes each outcome has an even chance of happening. For example, when you toss a coin, heads and tails are equally likely. They have an even chance of happening.

2   A likelihood scale runs from impossible to certain, with an 'even chance' in the middle.

3   Probability uses numbers to measure the chance of an outcome happening.

4   All probabilities have a value from 0 to 1.

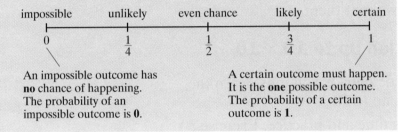

impossible	unlikely	even chance	likely	certain
0	$\frac{1}{4}$	$\frac{1}{2}$	$\frac{3}{4}$	1

An impossible outcome has **no** chance of happening. The probability of an impossible outcome is **0**.

A certain outcome must happen. It is the **one** possible outcome. The probability of a certain outcome is **1**.

5 Multiplication and division

Four hundred years ago most people did not need to multiply and divide.

Today most people do need to multiply and divide.

Calculators can help you, but you also need to be able to multiply and divide without them.

5.1 Multiplication up to 10×10

To multiply and divide **quickly** you must learn the multiplication tables up to 10×10.

Learning them takes time and practice. Exercise **5A** contains activities to help you practise.

Exercise 5A

1   Work out the following:
   (a) 3×7 **(b)** 5×9 **(c)** 2×6 **(d)** 7×8 **(e)** 6×5
   (f) 9×10 **(g)** 4×7 **(h)** 6×0 **(i)** 8×1 **(j)** 1×1

2   **Activity** You need a set of cards numbered 1 to 10, a watch which shows seconds and a copy of the multiplication table you wish to practise, for example the 6 times multiplication table.

   - Shuffle the cards and then turn one over. For each card that is turned over write down its number and multiply it by 6.
   - Time how long it takes you to do all ten cards and then check your answers.
   - Do this several times.

   If you can beat 30 seconds you are doing well.

3 Activity You need a set of cards numbered 1 to 10.

- Shuffle the cards.
- Turn over the top two cards and multiply together their numbers.
- Turn over the next two cards and multiply together their numbers.
- Continue until you have used all ten cards.
- Add together your five answers to get a total.
- Do this several times then try to answer the following questions.

$3 \times 7 = 21$
$8 \times 2 = 16$
$10 \times 5 = 50$
$6 \times 1 = 6$
$4 \times 9 = 36$

Total 129

(a) What is the smallest total you could make?

(b) What is the largest total you could make?

4 Activity This is a game for two players.
You need a dice.

Player 1
- Roll the dice twice. Multiply the two numbers together.

Player 2
- Roll the dice three times.
- Multiply two of the three numbers together to try to beat Player 1's total.

The player with the higher total gets a point.

- Do this five times then change places.

The player with the highest number of points, after all ten go's wins.

You can use your calculator to practise your times tables. See page 235.

5.2 Multiples

This is the 3 times multiplication table:

The answers 3, 6, 9, 12, 15, 18,...
are called the **multiples** of 3.

Multiply 3 by 1 to get the first multiple, 3.

Multiply 3 by 2 to get the second multiple, 6.

You only need to learn the 3 times multiplication table up to 10×3 but it actually goes on for ever!
That means the multiples of 3 also go on for ever.

$1 \times 3 = 3$
$2 \times 3 = 6$
$3 \times 3 = 9$
$4 \times 3 = 12$
$5 \times 3 = 15$

These are the multiples of 3

$28 \times 3 = 84$
$29 \times 3 = 87$

$28 \times 3 = 84$ so 84 is a multiple of 3

■ **The multiples of 3 are the answers in the 3 times multiplication table.**

You can find the multiples of 3 by multiplying 3 by 1, 2, 3, 4, 5, ...
They go on forever: 3, 6, 9, 12, 15, ... , 84, 87, ...

If you colour the multiples of 3 on a number line you colour every third number.

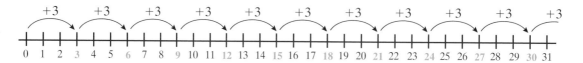

Here's another way to find the multiples of 3: write the counting numbers out in rows of 3 starting with the number 1.

1	2	3
4	5	6
7	8	9
10	11	12
13	14	15
16	17	

The numbers in the right hand column are multiples of 3

Example 1

Which multiples of 4 are between 30 and 50?

Write out the counting numbers up to 50 in rows of 4.

The multiples of 4 between 30 and 50 are 32, 36, 40, 44, 48.

If you know the 4 times table well you can start with $4 \times 8 = 32$ then count on in fours on a number line, or in your head:

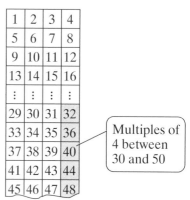

1	2	3	4
5	6	7	8
9	10	11	12
13	14	15	16
⋮	⋮	⋮	⋮
29	30	31	32
33	34	35	36
37	38	39	40
41	42	43	44
45	46	47	48

Multiples of 4 between 30 and 50

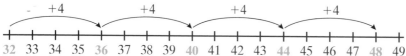

Exercise 5B

1 Which of these numbers are multiples of 3?

(a) 15   (b) 27   (c) 19   (d) 12   (e) 22   (f) 31
(g) 48   (h) 43   (i) 45   (j) 38   (k) 39   (l) 42

2   Which of these numbers are multiples of 4?

  (a) 15   **(b)** 16   **(c)** 32   **(d)** 31   **(e)** 24   **(f)** 36
  (g) 43   **(h)** 48   **(i)** 47   **(j)** 39   **(k)** 27   **(l)** 44

3   **(a)** Write out the multiples of 5 as far as 75.
  (b) There is an easy way to decide if a number
        is a multiple of 5 by looking at the units
        digit.
        What do you think it is?

1	2	3	4	5
6	7	8	9	10
11	12			

Multiples of 5

4   Use your rule from question **3(b)** to decide which of
    these numbers are multiples of 5.

  (a) 85   **(b)** 72   **(c)** 90   **(d)** 65   **(e)** 70   **(f)** 99
  (g) 110   **(h)** 125   **(i)** 104   **(j)** 360   **(k)** 275   **(l)** 341

5   Which multiples of 6 are between 50 and 80?

6   Which multiples of 7 are between 60 and 100?

7   Which multiples of 8 are less than 50?

8   These numbers are multiples of 3: 75, 78, 81, 84
    What are the next four multiples of 3?

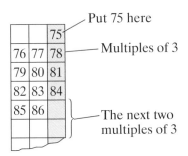

Put 75 here

Multiples of 3

The next two multiples of 3

or use a number line

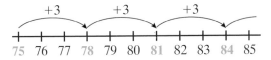

 9   These numbers are multiples of 4: 56, 60, 64, 68
    What are the next four multiples of 4?

10 These numbers are multiples of 6: 72, 78, 84, 90
    What are the next four multiples of 6?

11 **(a)** These pupils have each chosen a number from the board. Which number has each pupil chosen?

My number is a multiple of 7

My number is a multiple of 3 and 5

Jason

Ruchi

My number is a multiple of 2 between 15 and 20

My number is a multiple of 3 and 4

Sophie

Tim

What's my number?

25   12
    9   16
15   14

(b) Make up a puzzle like this and ask a friend to solve it.

5.3 Even and odd numbers

■ **The multiples of 2 are called EVEN numbers.**

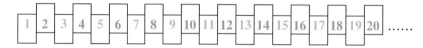

1 2 3 4 5 6 7 8 9 10 11 12 13 14 15 16 17 18 19 20 ......

The other whole numbers are called ODD numbers.

Exercise 5C

1 **Activity** You need a hundred square. Colour in all the even numbers on a hundred square.

(a) What do you notice about the pattern you get?

(b) What do you notice about the units digit of the even numbers?

(c) What do you notice about the units digit of the odd numbers?

You can read about the units digit on page 19

2 Write down all the even numbers less than 20.

3 Write down all the odd numbers less than 10.

4 What are the even numbers between 21 and 31?

5 What are the even numbers between 61 and 71?

6 What are the odd numbers between 50 and 60?

7 What are the odd numbers between 31 and 41?

8 What is the next even number after:

(**a**) 3 (**b**) 43 (**c**) 17 (**d**) 57 (**e**) 69 (**f**) 46

(**g**) 32 (**h**) 91 (**i**) 38 (**j**) 0 (**k**) 20 (**l**) 21?

Remember: the *next* even number *after* 46

9 What is the next odd number after:

(**a**) 4 (**b**) 28 (**c**) 18 (**d**) 38 (**e**) 64 (**f**) 71

(**g**) 47 (**h**) 8 (**i**) 55 (**j**) 39 (**k**) 23 (**l**) 24?

Remember: the *next* odd number *after* 71

10 What is the last even number before:

(**a**) 39 (**b**) 27 (**c**) 53 (**d**) 48 (**e**) 26 (**f**) 99?

11 What is the last odd number before:

(**a**) 22 (**b**) 36 (**c**) 40 (**d**) 43 (**e**) 27 (**f**) 100?

12 These pupils are each describing their number in a lottery. Which number does each pupil have?

Mine is an even number between 10 and 20

Mine is the last odd number before 40

Jason

Ruchi

Mine is the next even number after 47

Mine is the next odd number after 49

Sophie

Tim

5.4 Square numbers

You can arrange 9 square tiles to make a 3×3 square. 9 is called a **square number**.

You can't arrange 8 tiles to make a square so 8 is *not* a square number.

9 is a square number.

$3 \times 3 = 9$

$2 \times 4 = 8$ $1 \times 8 = 8$

8 is not a square number.

■ **When you multiply a whole number by itself you get a square number.**

$1 \times 1 = 1$, $2 \times 2 = 4$, $3 \times 3 = 9$, $4 \times 4 = 16$,
$5 \times 5 = 25 \dots$

1, 4, 9, 16, 25, ... are square numbers.

Exercise 5D

Use square tiles or squared paper for this exercise.

Which of these are square numbers?

1 10	**2** 16	**3** 20	**4** 4	**5** 15	**6** 18
7 1	**8** 25	**9** 49	**10** 36	**11** 80	**12** 100

13 There are another three square numbers less than 100, find them.

5.5 Multiplying by 10 and by 100

All multiples of 10 have zero units. For example:

10   20   30   40   50   60 100   110   120   130

30 has zero units   120 has zero units

■ **To multiply a whole number by 10 move each digit one column to the left and put 0 in the units column.**

$24 \times 10 = 240$

There is also a quick way to multiply by 100:

$100 = 10 \times 10$ so you can multiply by 10 and then by 10 again.

$100 = 10 \times 10$
So $24 \times 100 = 24 \times 10 \times 10$
So $24 \times 100 = 2400$

■ **To multiply a whole number by 100 move each digit two columns to the left, then put 0s in the hundreds and units columns.**

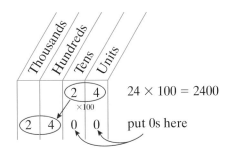

$24 \times 100 = 2400$

put 0s here

Exercise 5E

1 Which of these numbers are multiples of 10?
   (a) 80   **(b)** 74   **(c)** 148   **(d)** 270   **(e)** 138
   (f) 520   **(g)** 1760   **(h)** 2486   **(i)** 1000   **(j)** 305

2 Find
   (a) 23×10 **(b)** 39×10 **(c)** 83×10
   (d) 15×10 **(e)** 76×10 **(f)** 90×10
   (g) 154×10 **(h)** 342×10 **(i)** 270×10
   (j) 109×10 **(k)** 100×10 **(l)** 0×10 —— Does the rule work for 0×10?

3 Find
   (a) 32×100 **(b)** 93×100 **(c)** 38×100
   (d) 4×100 **(e)** 87×100 **(f)** 80×100
   (g) 15×100 **(h)** 10×100 **(i)** 99×100
   (j) 73×100 **(k)** 100×100 **(l)** 0×100 —— Does the rule work for 0×100?

5.6 Multiplication problems up to 10×10

Example 2

Sangita bought four books costing £8 each.
How much did she pay in total?

Total cost $= 4 \times £8$
$= £32$

Exercise 5F

1 Gigi bought five puzzle books costing £3 each.
   How much did she pay in total?

2 Severine gets £4 pocket money a week from her
   mother. Her mother owes Severine pocket money for
   five weeks.
   How much money does her mother owe Severine?

3 Susanne bought 7 packs of yoghurt.
Each pack contained 4 pots of yoghurt.
How many pots of yoghurt did Susanne buy altogether?

4 In Michele's classroom there are eight tables with four children sat at each table.
How many children are there in Michele's classroom?

5 Loïc bought three packs of six cassettes.
  (a) How many cassettes did he buy?
  (b) Each pack of cassettes cost £8.

    How much did he pay in total?

6 Sandrine bought three packs of fruit juice. Each pack cost £4 and contained 9 cartons of fruit juice.
  (a) How many cartons of fruit juice did she buy?
  (b) How much did she pay in total?

7 Ronan is buying the drinks for a children's party.
He needs enough lemonade to fill 65 glasses.

He knows that each bottle of lemonade will fill nine glasses so he buys 6 bottles.

Write down the multiplication you need to get your answer.

Has he bought enough?

8 Laurent is organising the food for the party. He needs enough sausages and bread rolls to make 31 hot dogs. He buys 4 packs of 8 sausages and 5 packs of 6 bread rolls.

  (a) Has he bought enough sausages?
  (b) Has he bought enough bread rolls?

9 Every day François does the following exercises.

    9 press ups
    6 sit ups
    7 step ups
    8 stretches
    5 star jumps

How many of each exercise does François do in a week?

10 These pupils have made up ways to remember their locker numbers.

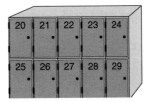

(a) Which locker does each pupil have?

My number is in the 4 and the 7 times tables

Marc

My number is in the multiplication table for 9

My number is in the 10 times table

Jo

My number is in the multiplication tables of 4 and 8

You multiply a number by itself to get mine

Adrian   Rebecca   Ray

(b) Make up a puzzle like this and ask your friends to solve it.

5.7 Dividing up to 100 ÷ 10

12 pupils are put into 4 teams.

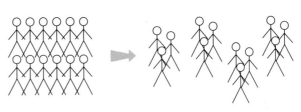

How many pupils are in each team?
You write this as a division: $12 \div 4 = 3$

You can think of division as the opposite of multiplication.
4 teams of 3 pupils is 12 pupils altogether so: $4 \times 3 = 12$

If 12 pupils are put into 3 teams:

This is the same as
$3 \times 4 = 12$

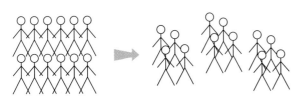

Each team gets 4 pupils: $12 \div 3 = 4$
3 teams of 4 pupils is 12 pupils altogether so: $3 \times 4 = 12$

■ $3 \times 4 = 12$ so $12 \div 3 = 4$ and $12 \div 4 = 3$

Another way of thinking of $12 \div 4$ is
'How many fours are there in twelve?'

$$\underbrace{4 + 4 + 4}_{} = 12$$

There are 3 fours in 12

so $12 \div 4 = 3$

Example 3

What is $32 \div 8$

$$4 \times 8 = 32 \quad \text{so} \quad 32 \div 8 = 4$$

Think of the 8 times
multiplication table.
$$1 \times 8 = 8$$
$$2 \times 8 = 16$$
$$3 \times 8 = 24$$
$$\boxed{4 \times 8 = 32}$$
so $\boxed{32 \div 8 = 4}$

Exercise 5G

1 Find:

   (a) $12 \div 2$ (b) $10 \div 5$ (c) $8 \div 2$ (d) $15 \div 3$

   (e) $8 \div 4$ (f) $6 \div 3$ (g) $16 \div 4$ (h) $15 \div 5$

   (i) $20 \div 2$ (j) $9 \div 3$ (k) $20 \div 4$ (l) $20 \div 5$

2 (a) $18 \div 2$ (b) $28 \div 4$ (c) $18 \div 3$ (d) $30 \div 5$

   (e) $36 \div 4$ (f) $16 \div 2$ (g) $45 \div 5$ (h) $27 \div 3$

   (i) $14 \div 2$ (j) $21 \div 3$ (k) $40 \div 5$ (l) $32 \div 4$

3 (a) $14 \div 7$ (b) $18 \div 6$ (c) $16 \div 8$ (d) $27 \div 9$

   (e) $30 \div 10$ (f) $24 \div 6$ (g) $21 \div 7$ (h) $50 \div 10$

   (i) $18 \div 9$ (j) $36 \div 9$ (k) $35 \div 7$ (l) $32 \div 8$

4 (a) $42 \div 6$ (b) $48 \div 8$ (c) $56 \div 7$ (d) $54 \div 9$

   (e) $80 \div 10$ (f) $63 \div 7$ (g) $72 \div 8$ (h) $54 \div 6$

   (i) $72 \div 9$ (j) $100 \div 10$ (k) $42 \div 7$ (l) $56 \div 8$

Example 4

Jim bought a pack of 6 cassettes for £18.
How much did each cassette cost?

Here you must divide the cost of £18 between
the 6 cassettes.

$$\text{Cost of each cassette} = £18 \div 6$$
$$= £3$$

Think of the 6 times
multiplication table.
$$1 \times 6 = 6$$
$$2 \times 6 = 12$$
$$\boxed{3 \times 6 = 18}$$
so $\boxed{18 \div 6 = 3}$

Example 5

A baker has 20 doughnuts to put into packets.
Each packet will hold 5 doughnuts.
How many packets can she fill?

Here you must work out how many fives there are in 20.

The baker can fill $= 20 \div 5$ packets

$= 4$ packets

Think of the 5 times
multiplication table.
$1 \times 5 = 5$
$2 \times 5 = 10$
$3 \times 5 = 15$
$\boxed{4 \times 5 = 20}$
so $\boxed{20 \div 5 = 4}$

Exercise 5H

1 Ahmed bought a set of 3 CDs for £24.
How much did each CD cost?

2 A hen keeper put 48 eggs into boxes.
Each box held 6 eggs when full.
How many boxes did he fill?

3 Jennifer swam nine lengths of a swimming pool in
27 minutes.
How long did she take to swim each length?

4 A class of 28 pupils were told by their teacher to get
into groups of four.
How many groups did they make?

5 A caretaker set out 56 chairs in 7 equal rows.
How many chairs did he put in each row?

6 Seven people shared the cost of hiring a hall for a party.
The hall cost £49 to hire.
How much did each person pay?

7 Four pupils ran a stall selling biscuits to raise money
for charity. At the end of the day they had 28 biscuits
left which they shared equally amongst themselves.
How many biscuits did each pupil get?

8 **(a)** Mrs Lamb is a French teacher. She has a lesson
which lasts for 30 minutes. She plans 5 activities on
which each pupil spends the same amount of time.
How long does each pupil spend on each activity?

(b) There are 35 pupils in the class. She puts the
pupils into 5 equal groups to move around the
activities. How many pupils does she put into each
group?

9 Mr Farmer runs a country dance club. For a square dance he puts the dancers into groups of 8. For other dances he puts the dancers into groups of 6. There are 24 dancers in his club.

   (a) How many groups does he have for a square dance?

   (b) How many groups does he have for other dances?

10 These pupils have made up questions using division.

   (a) What is the answer to each pupil's question?

   (b) Make up a question like this and ask your friends to answer it.

5.8 Multiplication and division problems up to 10 × 10

In Exercise 5I you must decide whether to multiply or divide to get the answer.

Exercise 5I

1 A plumber bought six washers costing 8p each. What was the total cost?

2 A holidaymaker bought five films for £15. How much did each film cost?

3 A fruitpacker put 54 peaches into packets. Each packet held 6 peaches. How many packets did he fill?

4 A man bought 3 books of 8 stamps.
How many stamps did he buy in total?

5 Each week Linda does the following
exercises:

Remember
There are 7 days in
a week.

70 press ups
35 sit ups
42 step ups
63 stretches.

She does the same number of each exercise
every day.
How many of each exercise does she do in a
day?

6 Bruno is organizing a barbecue.
He buys 5 packs of 8 sausages and
7 packs of 6 bread rolls.
How many hot dogs can he make?

7 Serafim needs 54 glasses for a party.
He decides to hire the glasses.
The glasses come in boxes of 9.
How many boxes does he need?

8 Jason is running a tombola.
He uses fifty tickets numbered 1 to 50.
He gives a prize for each ticket in the five times
multiplication table and a prize for each ticket in
the seven times multiplication table.
Which ticket should win two prizes?

9 Ruchi bought four packs of 3 cassettes.
Each pack cost £6.

(a) How many cassettes did she buy?
(b) How much did she pay altogether?
(c) What was the cost of each cassette?

10 Priya bought four packs of socks.
Each pack contained 3 pairs of socks and cost £6.

(a) What was the cost of each pair of socks?
(b) How many pairs of socks did she buy?
(c) What was the total cost?

5.9 Remainders

■ **When dividing 17p between 3 people,**
you can give each person 5p.
2p remains which you cannot divide by 3.
2p is called the remainder.

Use the 3 times table . . .

$5 \times 3 = 15$ so each person gets 5p

$1 \times 3 = 3$
$2 \times 3 = 6$
$3 \times 3 = 9$ just under 17
$4 \times 3 = 12$
$5 \times 3 = \textcircled{15}$
$6 \times 3 = 18$
more than 17

The remainder is the difference between 17 and 15.

$17 - 15 = 2$

You write $17 \div 3 = 5$ remainder 2.

> You can check your
> answer by doing
> $3 \times 5 + 2 = 17$

Example 6

What is $39 \div 8$?   Use the 8 times table . . .

$4 \times 8 = 32$ so $39 \div 8 = 4$ remainder $39 - 32$
$= 4$ remainder 7

$1 \times 8 = 8$
$2 \times 8 = 16$
$3 \times 8 = 24$ less than 39
$4 \times 8 = \textcircled{32}$
$5 \times 8 = 40$

more than 39

Exercise 5J

1 (a) $11 \div 2$ (b) $16 \div 3$ (c) $17 \div 5$ (d) $14 \div 4$
   (e) $11 \div 3$ (f) $26 \div 5$ (g) $39 \div 5$ (h) $29 \div 4$
   (i) $17 \div 2$ (j) $23 \div 3$ (k) $25 \div 4$ (l) $48 \div 5$

2 (a) $20 \div 6$ (b) $19 \div 8$ (c) $39 \div 9$ (d) $30 \div 7$
   (e) $33 \div 6$ (f) $19 \div 7$ (g) $29 \div 8$ (h) $21 \div 9$
   (i) $25 \div 6$ (j) $49 \div 9$ (k) $42 \div 8$ (l) $27 \div 7$

In Exercises **5H** and **5I** the numbers were chosen so there
were no remainders in the division sums. Problems in real
life are rarely like that and you have to decide what to do.

Example 7

A hen keeper has 50 eggs to put
into boxes.
Each box holds 6 eggs.
How many boxes can she fill?

$50 \div 6 = 8$ remainder 2.

The hen keeper can fill 8 boxes.
She has 2 eggs left over.

Example 8

A group of 23 people are going to a restaurant by taxi.
Each taxi can take 4 passengers.
How many taxis should they order?

$23 \div 4 = 5$ remainder 3.

If they order 5 taxis there will not be room for 3 people.
They must order 6 taxis.

Exercise 5K

In this exercise you need to decide what is a sensible
answer.

1   A fruit grower has 35 apples to put into packets.
    Each packet will hold 4 apples.
    How many packets can he fill?

2   A group of 28 girl guides are going camping.
    Each tent will sleep 6 people.
    How many tents do they need to take?

3   A group of 13 people go to a restaurant for a meal.
    Each table will seat 4 people.
    How many tables do they need?

4   A baker is putting gingerbread men into bags.
    He has 20 gingerbread men and he puts 3 in
    each bag.
    How many bags can he fill?

5   Elspeth wants to post 68 Christmas cards.
    How many books of 10 stamps must she buy?

6 A games teacher has a class of 27 pupils.
She wants them in equal groups for an activity.
Should she ask them to get into groups of 3, 4 or 5?

7 Gemima has to make at least 50 hot dogs for a party.

(a) How many packets of 8 sausages must she buy?

(b) How many packets of 6 rolls must she buy?

(c) How many hot dogs can she make?

5.10 Factors

When 6 is divided by any of the numbers 1, 2, 3 or 6 there
is no remainder.

The numbers 1, 2, 3 and 6 are called **factors** of 6.
A factor is always a whole number.

■ **The factors of a number are those numbers that divide
exactly into it leaving no remainder.**
For example, 1, 2, 3 and 6 are the factors of 6.
A factor is always a whole number.

You can think of factors in several other ways:

1 In the multiplication tables 6 appears
as an answer in the tables for 1, 2, 3
and 6.
It does not appear as an answer in any
other tables.
The numbers 1, 2, 3 and 6 are called
the factors of 6.

$1 \times 1 = 1$ $1 \times 2 = 2$ $1 \times 3 = 3$ $1 \times 6 = ⑥$
$2 \times 1 = 2$ $2 \times 2 = 4$ $2 \times 3 = ⑥$ $1 \times 6 = 12$
$3 \times 1 = 3$ $3 \times 2 = ⑥$ $3 \times 3 = 9$
$4 \times 1 = 4$ $4 \times 2 = 8$
$5 \times 1 = 5$
$6 \times 1 = ⑥$
$7 \times 1 = 7$

2 The number 6 is a **multiple** of 1, 2, 3 and 6.
The numbers 1, 2, 3 and 6 are called the factors of 6.

3 If you take 6 square tiles and put them
together to form a rectangle, you can do
this in two ways.
The numbers 1, 2, 3 and 6 are called the
factors of 6.

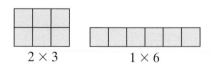

2×3 1×6

Example 9

What are the factors of 12?

Find all the ways you can arrange 12 square tiles together to form a rectangle.

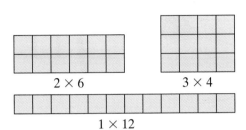

2 × 6   3 × 4

1 × 12

Hint: If you do not have square tiles you could use cubes or squared paper.

The factors of 12 are 1, 2, 3, 4, 6 and 12.

Example 10

Is 7 a factor of 21?

Write down the multiples of 7:

$$7, 14, \textcircled{21}, 28, \ldots$$

21 is a multiple of 7 so yes 7 is a factor of 21.

Or try to arrange 21 square tiles in a rectangle with one side of length 7.

Exercise 5L

1 You need square tiles or cubes or squared paper for this question.
What are the factors of:

(**a**) 10   (**b**) 14   (**c**) 18   (**d**) 7   (**e**) 20   (**f**) 9
(**g**) 25   (**h**) 16   (**i**) 22   (**j**) 24   (**k**) 28   (**l**) 30

2 Which of these are true and which are false?

(**a**) 5 is a factor of 25   (**b**) 3 is a factor of 15
(**c**) 4 is a factor of 9   (**d**) 6 is a factor of 48
(**e**) 7 is a factor of 28   (**f**) 8 is a factor of 26
(**g**) 9 is a factor of 28   (**h**) 7 is a factor of 49
(**i**) 9 is a factor of 63   (**j**) 8 is a factor of 24
(**k**) 10 is a factor of 90   (**l**) 2 is a factor of 18

3 These pupils have each chosen a number from the board. Which number has each pupil chosen?

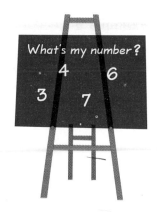

What's my number?

4   6

3   7

My number is a factor of 8 and 12

Jason

My number is not a factor of 12

Ruchi

My number is a factor of 8

Sophie

My number is a factor of 9

Tim

5.11 Multiplying a 2-digit number by a 1-digit number without a calculator

To do multiplications like 28×3 without a calculator ...
... you need to be able to do calculations like 20×3.

You know that $2 \times 3 = 6$.
Think of this as three 2p coins.

$2 \times 3 = 6$
$20 \times 3 = 60$

Now replace each 2p coin with a 20p coin.
So $20 \times 3 = 60$.

Exercise 5M

Find:

1 (a) 40×2 (b) 30×2 (c) 20×4
   (d) 50×3 (e) 60×2 (f) 70×2
   (g) 60×3 (h) 70×4 (i) 80×3
   (j) 90×4 (k) 80×5 (l) 50×4

2 (a) 30×7 (b) 60×6 (c) 50×7
   (d) 30×8 (e) 40×9 (f) 70×6
   (g) 90×6 (h) 60×7 (i) 80×7
   (j) 80×9 (k) 80×8 (l) 90×7

3 (a) 40×8 (b) 90×3 (c) 60×5
   (d) 70×7 (e) 80×4 (f) 4×60
   (g) 5×40 (h) 3×70 (i) 3×30
   (j) 5×90 (k) 8×90 (l) 9×90

Hint: think of this as 60×4

Making multiplying easier

To do 28×3

Think of 28 as 20 and 8

You know $20 \times 3 = 60$
and $8 \times 3 = 24$ $\Big\}$ add the answers
so $28 \times 3 = 84$

The idea is to split a hard multiplication into two easier ones.

A good way to set out your working is like this

$20 \times 3 = 60$
$8 \times 3 = 24$
$28 \times 3 = 84$

You may already know this way of setting out your working. Try both methods to see how they compare

$$\begin{array}{r} 2\,8 \\ \times\ 3 \\ \hline 8\,4 \\ \scriptstyle 2 \end{array}$$

Exercise 5N

Find:

1. (a) 24×3 (b) 37×2 (c) 26×4
   (d) 27×3 (e) 17×5 (f) 4×18 — Hint: think of this as 18×4
   (g) 2×39 (h) 64×3 (i) 3×76
   (j) 5×45 (k) 63×4 (l) 36×5

2. (a) 23×6 (b) 42×4 (c) 29×7
   (d) 37×8 (e) 64×9 (f) 6×78 — Hint: think of this as 78×6
   (g) 7×39 (h) 5×54 (i) 87×6
   (j) 72×7 (k) 9×57 (l) 98×9

3. Nadia bought 4 pencils for 23p each.
   How much did she have to pay?

4. In a school there are 6 classes in year 7.
   Each class has 29 pupils in it.
   How many pupils are there in year 7?

5. Jasmine bought 7 packs of cola
   for a party.
   Each pack contained 24 cans.
   How many cans did she buy?

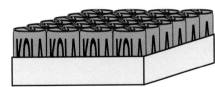

6. A school ordered 8 boxes of erasers.
   Each box contained 36 erasers.
   How many erasers did the school order?

7. Every day Alan cycles to work and back.
   Each day he cycles 18 miles.
   How many miles does he cycle in a 5-day working
   week?

8 Choose any three digits.
Arrange them as a 2-digit number multiplied by a
1-digit number and do the multiplication.
Try other arrangements of the same digits.

For example ...

7 4 6

$67 \times 4 = 268$
$76 \times 4 = 304$

(a) How many different arrangements are there?

(b) Which arrangement gives the biggest answer?

(c) Which arrangement gives the smallest answer?

(d) Try other sets of digits.

(e) Can you spot any rules to help you answer parts
(b) and (c)?

Summary of key points

1 The multiples of 3 are the answers in the 3 times multiplication table.
You can find the multiples of 3 by multiplying 3 by 1, 2, 3, 4, 5, ...
They go on forever: 3, 6, 9, 12, 15, ..., 84, 87, ...

2 The multiples of 2 are called **EVEN** numbers.

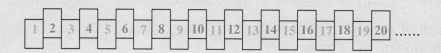

The other whole numbers are called **ODD** numbers.

3 When you multiply a whole number by itself you get a square number.

$1 \times 1 = 1$, $2 \times 2 = 4$, $3 \times 3 = 9$, $4 \times 4 = 16$, $5 \times 5 = 25$ ...

1, 4, 9, 16, 25, ... are square numbers.

4 To multiply a whole number by 10 move
each digit one column to the left and
put 0 in the units column.

$24 \times 10 = 240$

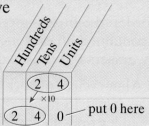

5 To multiply a whole number by 100 move each digit two columns to the left, then put 0 in the hundreds column and another 0 in the units column.

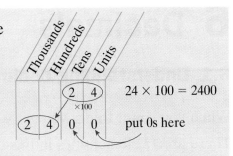

$24 \times 100 = 2400$

put 0s here

6 $3 \times 4 = 12$ so $12 \div 3 = 4$ and $12 \div 4 = 3$

7 When dividing 17p between 3 people, you can give each person 5p. 2p remains which you cannot divide by 3. The 2p is called the remainder.

8 The factors of a number are those numbers that divide exactly into it leaving no remainder. For example, 1, 2, 3 and 6 are the factors of 6. A factor is always a whole number.

6 Decimals

6.1 Understanding decimals

When you count things you get whole number values:

There are 12 clementines in this bag:

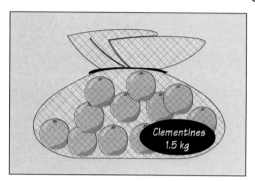

8 runners ran this race:

This bag weighs 1.5 kilogrammes.
You say 'one point five kilos'.

The winner took 20.51 seconds.
You say 'twenty point five one'
seconds.

Measurements like these are **not** whole numbers.
1.5 and 20.51 are **decimal numbers**.

- **In a decimal number the decimal point separates the
  whole number part from the part that is less than one:**

decimal point

1.5

1 is the whole
number part

.5 is the part
less than one

This place value diagram will help you understand
what 1.5 means:

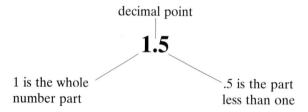

The whole number part is 1
There is 1 unit

The part less than one is .5
There are 5 tenths

5 tenths can
also be written
as a fraction:

$\frac{5}{10}$

There is more
about fractions
on page 121

Example 1

This thermometer shows 38.2°C.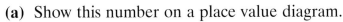

(a) Show this number on a place value diagram.

(b) Write down the value of each digit.

(a) The place value diagram is:

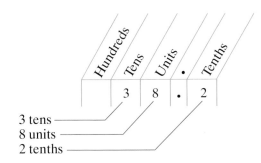

(b) The value of the 3 is 3 tens.
The value of the 8 is 8 units.
The value of the 2 is 2 tenths.

Example 2

Write down the value of the underlined digit in each decimal number:

(a) 2<u>8</u>.2   **(b)** 3.<u>2</u>   **(c)** <u>4</u>23.5   **(d)** 59.<u>4</u>

(a) 8 units   **(b)** 2 tenths   **(c)** 4 hundreds   **(d)** 4 tenths

Exercise 6A

1 Draw a decimal place value diagram like the one in Example 1 and write in these numbers.

    (a) 39.2   **(b)** 5.6   **(c)** 53.8   **(d)** 129.7
    (e) 134.5   **(f)** 9.1   **(g)** 50.3   **(h)** 0.4

2 Write down the value of the digit underlined in each of these decimal numbers.

    (a) <u>3</u>2.5   **(b)** 1<u>6</u>.7   **(c)** 5.<u>8</u>   **(d)** <u>2</u>53.6
    (e) 19.<u>7</u>   **(f)** 0.<u>3</u>   **(g)** 27<u>5</u>.2   **(h)** 124.<u>5</u>

■ **You can also show decimal numbers with two decimal places in a place value diagram:**

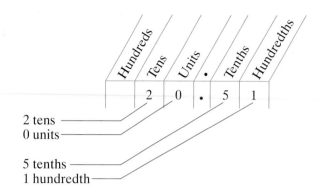

2 tens
0 units

5 tenths
1 hundredth

1 hundredth can also be written as a fraction:

$\frac{1}{100}$

Example 3

The calculator shows 214.06

(a) Show this number on a place value diagram.

(b) Write down the value of each digit.

(a) The place value diagram is:

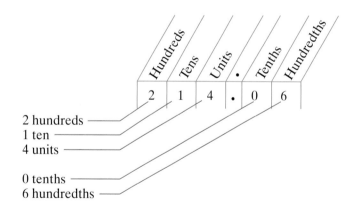

2 hundreds
1 ten
4 units

0 tenths
6 hundredths

Remember:
Put the whole number part in the diagram first.
Then put in the decimal part.

(b) The value of 2 is 2 hundreds.
   The value of 1 is 1 ten.
   The value of 4 is 4 units.
   The value of 0 is 0 tenths.
   The value of 6 is 6 hundredths.

Exercise 6B

1 Draw a place value diagram like the one in Example 3
and write in these numbers.

    (a) 23.4   **(b)** 5.21   **(c)** 28.5   **(d)** 123.8

    (e) 1.25   **(f)** 0.32   **(g)** 2.01   **(h)** 25.07

    (i) 0.07   **(j)** 520.06   **(k)** 17.58   **(l)** 0.09

2 Write down the value of the digit underlined in each of
these decimal numbers.

    (a) 2̲6.8   **(b)** 5̲3.2   **(c)** 15.7̲6   **(d)** 2.5̲3

    (e) 12.8̲3   **(f)** 9̲.28   **(g)** 6̲25.2   **(h)** 15̲2.8

    (i) 8.1̲5   **(j)** 2.5̲3   **(k)** 2̲.38   **(l)** 0.0̲4

3 **(a)** Use a calculator to calculate $0.1 + 0.1 + 0.1 + 0.1 + 0.1 + 0.1 + 0.1 + 0.1 + 0.1$
      What do you notice?

    (b) Use a calculator to calculate $0.01 + 0.01 + 0.01 + 0.01 + 0.01 + 0.01 + 0.01 + 0.01 + 0.01 + 0.01$
      What do you notice?

6.2 Money, money, money!

John has £1 and 52 pence.

You can write this in pounds as £1.52

■ **When you write money in pounds, the decimal point
separates the pounds from the pence.**

£1.52 pounds pence

Example 4

Work out the value of these coins in pounds.

(a)

(a) There are 3 pound coins: £3
The pence coins total
$20p + 20p + 50p = 90p$

The total value of the coins is
£3 + 90p

= £3.90

(b)

(b) There are £2 and 116p
116p = £1 and 16p
The total is £3 and 16p
= £3.16

(c)

(c) There are £2 and 1p
This is £2.01

Notice that it is not £2.10
– that is £2 and 10p!

The zero keeps the
1p in its correct
position.

Exercise 6C

1 Work out the total value of the coins in pounds.

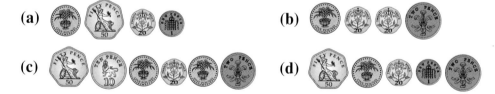

(a)   **(b)**

(c)   **(d)**

2 Work out the total value of the coins in pounds.

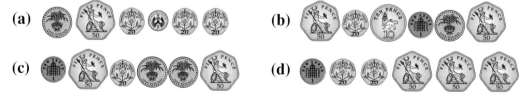

(a)   **(b)**

(c)   **(d)**

3 Work out the total value of the coins in pounds.

(a)   **(b)**

(c)   **(d)**

4 Work out the total value of the coins in pounds.

(a)

(b)

(c)

(d)

5 Work out the total value of the coins in pounds.

(a)

(b)

(c)

(d)

6 Omar has one each of the coins £1, 50p, 20p, 10p, 5p, 2p and 1p.
Write down which coins Omar could use to make:

(a) £1.52 (b) £1.11 (c) £1.83 (d) £0.32

(e) £1.88 (f) £1.35 (g) £1.70 (h) £1.37

(i) £0.06 (j) £0.75 (k) £1.16 (l) £0.08

7 (a) Philip has four coins, a £1, a 10p, a 50p and a 20p.
Work out the total value of his coins in pounds.

(b) Louise has three coins, a £1, a 2p and a 3p. Work out the total value of her coins in pounds.

(c) What is the total value, in pounds, of Philip's and Louise's coins?

8 Chris has these coins:

He needs to put exactly £1.85 in a slot machine for a train ticket.
The slot machine takes any coins.

Which coins could Chris put in the slot machine?
Write down all the different ways he could make £1.85 with his coins.

6.3 Adding and subtracting money amounts

You can add and subtract
sums of money.

Remember to keep the
decimal points lined up.

This lines up the units.

Example 5

Add together £23.40 and £34.25

Line up the decimal points: 23.40
The units will line up.   34.25
Put the point in the answer: ——————

Then add: 23.40
                       34.25
                       ——————
                       57.65

> Remember to add
> from the right.
>
> There is more about
> adding on page 38

Give your answer in pounds: £57.65

Example 6

Add £53.26 and £4.72
Show all your working.

Line up the units and   53.26
   the decimal points: 4.72
                      ——————
                      57.98

The total is £57.98

Exercise 6D

Work these out **without a calculator**.
Show all your working.

1   £10.32 + £25.26   **2**   £3.20 + £12.62

3   £4.20 + £5.50   **4**   £12.04 + £15.32

5 £25.14 + £13.35

6 £13.32 + £5.43

7 £7.42 + £6.35

8 £25.24 + £34.61

9 £12.23 + £8.74

10 £62.53 + £17.26

11 £6.04 + £12.55

12 £13.16 + £96.83

6.4 Adding and subtracting decimals

■ **When you add or subtract decimal numbers always line up the decimal points. This keeps the units in line.**

Example 7

Two children weigh 26.4 kg and 23.3 kg.
How much do they weigh altogether?

Line up the decimal points: 26.4
This lines up the units.   23.3
Put the point in the answer.   .

Add: 26.4
   23.3
   49.7

They weigh 49.7 kg altogether.

Example 8

Work out 3.2 + 14.36 + 22.24
Show all your working.

Line up the points: 3.2
   14.36
   22.24

Put the point in the answer: .

Add from the right: 3.2
   14.36
   22.24
   39.80
   1

The total is 39.80
You can leave off the last zero.
The answer is 39.8

Exercise 6E

Find:

1 2.3 + 1.4	**2** 41.6 + 35.2	**3** 24.6 + 23.3
4 152.8 + 315.1	**5** 13.5 + 2.4	**6** 17.25 + 3.42
7 16.32 + 13.57	**8** 5.2 + 2.38	**9** 53.47 + 25.3
10 52.5 + 6.29	**11** 10 + 3.9	**12** 16.2 + 3.74
13 124 + 3.79	**14** 3.6 + 0.27	**15** 5.8 + 2.4
16 4.29 + 2.31	**17** 16.28 + 23.52	**18** 5.2 + 3.4 + 1.2
19 3.2 + 12.3 + 4.48	**20** 12.07 + 5.4 + 2.32	

21 The temperature in Caerphilly at midnight was 8.7 degrees Celsius. By noon the temperature had gone up by 7.2 degrees Celsius.
What was the temperature at noon?

22 Megan cut lengths of 22.42 cm, 4.35 cm and 3.21 cm from some dowelling for her woodwork project.
Work out the total length of dowelling she cut.

Example 9

Jack collects £94.35 on his tombola stall.
He keeps £21.12 for the prizes.
How much money does he make?

You need to find £94.35 − £21.12

Line up the points:
$$\begin{array}{r} 94.35 \\ -\,21.12 \\ \hline \end{array}$$

Put the point in the answer:
$$\begin{array}{r} . \\ \hline \end{array}$$

Subtract from the right:
$$\begin{array}{r} 94.35 \\ -\,21.12 \\ \hline 73.23 \end{array}$$

He makes £73.23

There is more about subtracting on page 42

Example 10

Work out 64.3 − 21.18

Line up the points:

64.3
21.18

Put the point in the answer:

.

Add a zero to 64.3
Now subtract:

$64.\overset{2}{\cancel{3}}\overset{1}{0}$
21.18
43.12

The answer is 43.12

Exercise 6F

Find:

1 29.8 − 13.6   **2** 35.9 − 32.7   **3** 4.94 − 2.71

4 5.73 − 2.61   **5** 38.6 − 8.5   **6** 167.8 − 4.3

7 106.9 − 4.5   **8** 0.87 − 0.53   **9** 12.86 − 1.45

10 4.85 − 1.4   **11** 15.78 − 3.5   **12** 39.15 − 12

13 7.928 − 3.6   **14** 245.95 − 2.7   **15** 12.84 − 4.31

16 308.95 − 65.72 **17** 7.8 − 2.34   **18** 1 − 0.4

19 A cake weighed 2.55 kg. What was the weight of the cake after Sajid ate a slice that weighed 0.13 kg?

20 The temperature in Durham at noon was 9.8 degrees Celsius. By midnight the temperature had fallen by 5.3 degrees Celsius. What was the temperature at midnight?

21 Amy's packed case weighed 21.9 kg. To reduce the weight Amy removed a hairdryer weighing 0.7 kg and a pair of boots weighing 1.8 kg. Work out the new weight of the case.

22 James sawed a length of 0.35 metre from a one metre piece of wood. Work out the length of wood left over.

Summary of key points

1   In a decimal number the decimal point
separates the whole number part from
the part that is less than one.

decimal point

1.5

1 is the whole   .5 is the part
number part   less than one

2   You can also show decimal numbers with
two decimal places in a place value diagram.

Tens	Units	.	Tenths	Hundredths
2	0	.	5	1

3   When you write money in pounds
the decimal point separates the pounds
from the pence.

£1.52

pounds   pence

4   To add or subtract decimal numbers
always line up the decimal points.
This keeps the units in line.

$$\begin{array}{r} 26.4 \\ + \ 3.35 \\ \hline 43.12 \end{array}$$

7 Measuring

In this unit you will learn about measuring length, weight and time.

7.1 Measuring lengths

You measure short
lengths in centimetres,
or cm for short.

You measure medium
lengths in metres,
or m for short.

You measure longer
lengths in kilometres,
or km for short.

The little fingernail is about
1 cm wide.
You use a ruler to measure
short lengths.

A door is about 2 m high.
You use a tape measure to
measure medium lengths.

Three times round a football
pitch is about 1 km. You can
use a trundle wheel to
measure it!

Exercise 7A

1 You have a ruler, a tape measure and a trundle wheel. Which would you use to measure each of these distances?

The length of:

(a) a pencil **(b)** a road **(c)** a corridor
(d) a ladder **(e)** a garage **(f)** a tennis court
(g) a cricket bat handle **(h)** a nail
(i) the River Thames **(j)** a piece of chalk

The height of:

(k) a cupboard **(l)** the ceiling **(m)** a table lamp
(n) a door **(o)** a CD case **(p)** a mouse

The width of:

(q) a book **(r)** a bridge **(s)** a blackboard

2 Write down which units you would use for each part of question **1**. Write down cm, m or km.

3 Write down 3 things you would measure in:

(a) cm **(b)** m **(c)** km

7.2 Using a ruler

You can use a centimetre ruler to measure and draw short lengths:

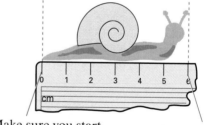

Make sure you start at 0 on the ruler.

This snail is 6 cm long.

Example 1

Draw a line 4 cm long.

Put a dot on the paper.

Draw a line to 4 cm.

Put 0 on the ruler against the dot. Make sure you start at 0.

Exercise 7B

You need a centimetre ruler.

1   Measure these lines:

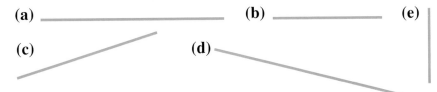

2   Draw these lines:

   (a) 3 cm   **(b)** 8 cm   **(c)** 1 cm   **(d)** 11 cm

3   Measure the width of each of your fingernails.
   Which is the closest to 1 cm?

4   Use your fingernail to find out roughly how long these
   lines are.
   Check your answers with a ruler.

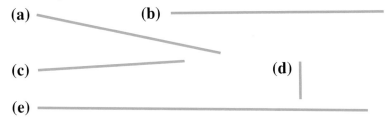

5   **(a)** Look at the red and blue lines on the right.
         Which one do you think is longest?
   (b) Measure each line in cm.
   (c) Which line is longest?
   (d) Make up a question like this of your own and ask
         someone else to solve it.

6   **Activity**   For 2 people.
   You need a metre rule or tape marked in cm and
   2 counters.

   •   The first person names a length up to 100 cm.
   •   The second person tries to place the counters that
       distance apart without using a ruler.
   •   The first person then measures the distance between
       the counters.

   Do this 5 times each.
   Who did best?

7.3 Longer and longer

■ **100 cm = 1 m**
   200 cm = 2 m
   300 cm = 3 m

Here is part of a tape measure:

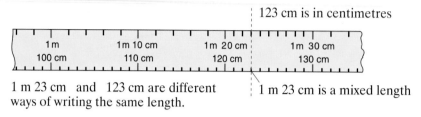

123 cm is in centimetres

1 m 23 cm and 123 cm are different
ways of writing the same length.

1 m 23 cm is a mixed length

Exercise 7C

You need a tape measure.

1 **Activity** Measure:
   (a) the width of a window in your classroom
   (b) the length of a table
   (c) the height of a cupboard
   (d) the width of the board
   (e) the width and length of the room.

2 Walk ten paces. Measure and record the distance you
   walked.

3 Find objects with lengths as close as possible to these
   lengths:
   2 m, 3 m 50 cm, 7 m

4 Which of these animals could fit into your classroom?
   (Assume the door is wide enough!)

Animal	Length
Whale	16 m
Snake	9 m
Shark	5 m 30 cm
Crocodile	3 m 20 cm

Example 2

(a) Write 2 m 36 cm in centimetres.

(b) Write 309 cm in metres and centimetres.

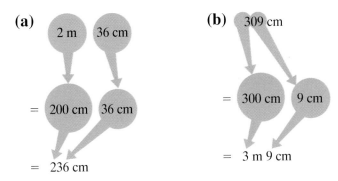

(a)

2 m   36 cm

= 200 cm   36 cm

= 236 cm

(b) 309 cm

= 300 cm   9 cm

= 3 m 9 cm

Example 3

Write these lengths in order of size:

   3 m 42 cm   3 m 37 cm   5 m 27 cm   1 m 29 cm

Start with the shortest.

First sort using the number of metres:

   1 m 29 cm   3 m 42 cm   3 m 37 cm   5 m 27 cm

                These both have 3 metres.

Then sort using the number of centimetres:

   1 m 29 cm   3 m 42 cm   3 m 37 cm   5 m 27 cm

   1 m 29 cm   3 m 37 cm   3 m 42 cm   5 m 27 cm

Exercise 7D

1   Write these mixed lengths in centimetres:

   (a) 3 m 20 cm   **(b)** 5 m 72 cm   **(c)** 8 m 12 cm
   (d) 10 m 15 cm   **(e)** 20 m 40 cm   **(f)** 14 m 3 cm

2   Write as mixed lengths in metres and centimetres:

   (a) 150 cm   **(b)** 235 cm   **(c)** 758 cm
   (d) 105 cm   **(e)** 307 cm   **(f)** 1250 cm
   (g) 3056 cm   **(h)** 4271 cm   **(i)** 3008 cm

3 Put these lengths in order of size.
Start with the shortest.

2 m 30 cm   2 m 25 cm   1 m 48 cm   1 m 32 cm   2 m 9 cm

4 This table shows the lengths of some animals.

Animal	Length
Gnu	210 cm
Zebra	216 cm
Cheetah	135 cm
Leopard	165 cm
Lion	178 cm

Put them in order of length, starting with the shortest.

5 Bradford's six jumps in the long jump final were:

8 m 17 cm, 7 m 94 cm, 9 m 3 cm, 8 m 9 cm, 7 m 87 cm, 7 m 81 cm

(a) Which was his longest jump?

(b) Put his jumps in order of size.
Start with the longest.

7.4 Kilometres

- **1000 m = 1 km**
  2000 m = 2 km

It takes me half an hour to walk to school. That must be 2 km

You can write long distances in metres or as a mixed length:

Example 4

Write in metres:

(a) 2 km 300 m   **(b)** 1 km 324 m   **(c)** 5 km 40 m

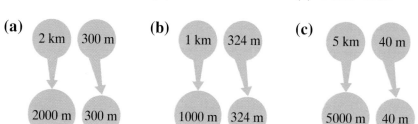

(a) 2 km   300 m → 2000 m   300 m
= 2300 m

(b) 1 km   324 m → 1000 m   324 m
= 1324 m

(c) 5 km   40 m → 5000 m   40 m
= 5040 m

Example 5

Write as a mixed length:

(a) 1900 m **(b)** 2070 m **(c)** 9003 m **(d)** 11 000 m

(a) 1 900 m **(b)** 2 070 m **(c)** 9 003 m **(d)** 11 000 m

| 1 km   900 m | 2 km   70 m | 9 km   3 m | 11 km   0 m |
| = 1 km 900 m | = 2 km 70 m | = 9 km 3 m | = 11 km |

Exercise 7E

1 Write in metres:

   (a) 3 km 230 m **(b)** 21 km 500 m **(c)** 15 km 370 m
   (d) 2 km 155 m **(e)** 10 km 40 m **(f)** 37 km 20 m
   (g) 1 km 45 m **(h)** 2 km 5 m

2 Write as a mixed length:

   (a) 2125 m **(b)** 4050 m **(c)** 14 406 m **(d)** 1008 m
   (e) 7030 m **(f)** 5250 m **(g)** 2000 m **(h)** 53 000 m
   (i) 12 500 m **(j)** 4600 m

3 Match each race to a distance.

Name of race   *Distance*

3000 m steeple chase	1 km 600 m
5000 metres	1 km 500 m
1500 metres	3 km
10 000 metres	5 km
4 × 400 m relay	10 km

4 Write down these rivers in order of length.
   Start with the longest.

   Trent   274 km   Thames 336 km
   Severn 338 km   Wye   209 km

7.5 Measuring weight

You use grams
to measure
light objects.

You use kilograms
to measure heavier
objects.

You use tonnes
to measure heavy
objects.

A piece of paper
weighs about 5 g.

A bag of sugar
weighs about 1 kg.

A small car
weighs about 1 t.

Exercise 7F

1 In what units would you weigh these objects?
Write grams, kilograms or tonnes.

(a) A sweet   (b) A bicycle   (c) A bus

(d) A sparrow   (e) A swan   (f) An elephant

(g) A brick   (h) Your exercise book   (i) A shoe

(j) A tie   (k) A coat   (l) A piano

(m) A whistle   (n) A chair   (o) A table

2 Write four things that you would weigh in each of these
units:

(a) tonnes   (b) kilograms   (c) grams

7.6 Mixing weights

■ **1000 g = 1 kg**

1000 kg = 1 t

Example 6

(a) Write 2360 g as a mixed weight.

(b) Write 4028 kg as a mixed weight

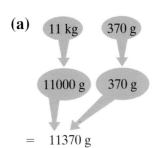

(a)

2 360 g

= 2000 g   360 g

= 2 kg   360 g

(b)

4 028 kg

= 4000 kg   28 kg

= 4 t   28 kg

Example 7

(a) Write 11 kg 370 g in grams.

(b) Write 5 t 45 kg in kg.

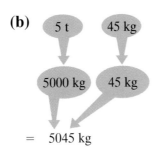

(a)

11 kg   370 g

11000 g   370 g

= 11370 g

(b)

5 t   45 kg

5000 kg   45 kg

= 5045 kg

Exercise 7G

1 Write in grams:
- **(a)** 3 kg
- **(b)** 6 kg 200 g
- **(c)** 9 kg 420 g
- **(d)** 3 kg 250 g
- **(e)** 8 kg 50 g
- **(f)** 10 kg 5 g

2 Write in kilograms:
- **(a)** 6 t
- **(b)** 4 t 500 kg
- **(c)** 3 t 120 kg
- **(d)** 9 t 170 kg
- **(e)** 7 t 40 kg
- **(f)** 11 t 9 kg

3 Write as a mixed weight:
- **(a)** 2750 g
- **(b)** 3500 g
- **(c)** 7570 g
- **(d)** 1050 g
- **(e)** 10 025 g
- **(f)** 4006 g
- **(g)** 4200 kg
- **(h)** 6050 kg
- **(i)** 10 010 kg

4   In a fishing competition the person who catches the greatest weight of fish is the winner.

The cards below show the weights of fish caught by the top 6 people in the competition.

Copy and complete the table.

Position in competition	Name of person	Weight of fish
1st		
2nd		
3rd		
4th		

Fiona
3 kg 450 g

Jeremy
2 kg 720 g

Jenna
3 kg 26 g

Veeran
2 kg 38 g

Burt
2 kg 98 g

Inam
3 kg 286 g

7.7 Reading scales

You need to be able to read scales like these to measure weights:

How to read a scale:

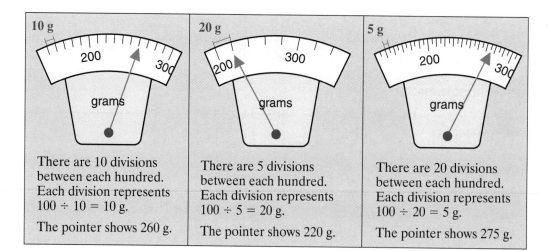

10 g	**20 g**	**5 g**
There are 10 divisions between each hundred. Each division represents $100 \div 10 = 10$ g.	There are 5 divisions between each hundred. Each division represents $100 \div 5 = 20$ g.	There are 20 divisions between each hundred. Each division represents $100 \div 20 = 5$ g.
The pointer shows 260 g.	The pointer shows 220 g.	The pointer shows 275 g.

Example 8

On this scale:

(a) What does each division represent?

(b) How much do the potatoes weigh?

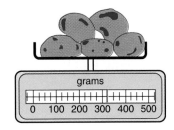

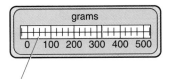

(a) There are 4 divisions between each hundred.
Each division represents 100 ÷ 4 = 25g.

(b) The pointer shows 325 g.
The potatoes weigh 325 g.

Exercise 7H

For each scale:

(a) What does each division represent?

(b) What weight does each pointer show?

1
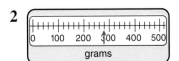

2
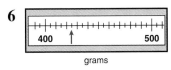

3
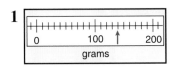

4
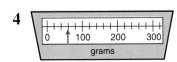

5
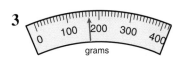

6
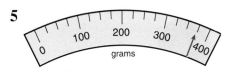

Read the measurements on these scales:

7
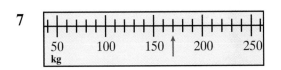

8
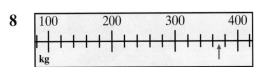

7.8 What time is it?

There are two kinds of clock:

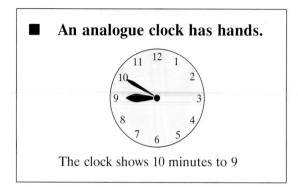

■ **An analogue clock has hands.**

The clock shows 10 minutes to 9

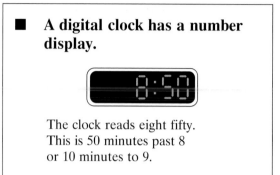

■ **A digital clock has a number display.**

The clock reads eight fifty.
This is 50 minutes past 8
or 10 minutes to 9.

You need to be able to read the time from both types of clock.

Reading analogue clocks:

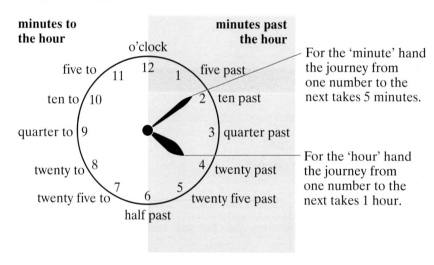

minutes to the hour

five to
ten to
quarter to
twenty to
twenty five to

o'clock

minutes past the hour

five past
ten past
quarter past
twenty past
twenty five past

half past

For the 'minute' hand the journey from one number to the next takes 5 minutes.

For the 'hour' hand the journey from one number to the next takes 1 hour.

Exercise 7I

1   Six pupils each read the time when they got home from school.

May — ten past four

Trish — quarter to five

Alice — twenty past four

Tim — twenty to five

Kunal — quarter past four

Petra — five minutes to five

Which clock is in each pupil's home?

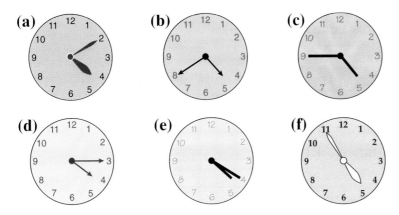

2 What is the time on each of these clocks?
Write your answer as you would say it.

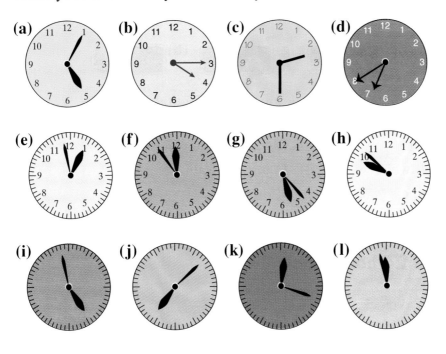

Reading digital clocks:

Digital clocks are easy to read.

This says five thirty
or half past 5.

This says ten twenty
or 20 minutes past
10.

This says one forty
or 40 minutes past 1
or 20 minutes to 2.

Exercise 7J

1 Copy and complete this table showing times up to five o'clock.

Analogue	Digital
Four o'clock	4:00
Five minutes past four	4:05
Ten minutes past four	4:10

2 Write down the times on these clocks as you would say them:

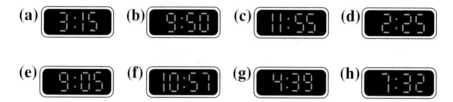

(a) 3:15 (b) 9:50 (c) 11:55 (d) 2:25

(e) 9:05 (f) 10:57 (g) 4:39 (h) 7:32

3 Write these times as they would appear on a digital clock.

(a) Five fifteen   (b) Twenty past seven

(c) Half past twelve   (d) Twenty to four

(e) Five to nine   (f) Midday

7.9 Using the 24-hour clock

This clock shows 7 o'clock.

7 o'clock in the morning is 7 am

7 o'clock in the evening is 7 pm

■ **You use am for times before midday.**

■ **You use pm for times after midday.**

Hint: a comes before p in the alphabet.

Some digital clocks use 24-hour time to show whether
it is before midday or after midday.

This shows 9.30 am   This shows 9.30 pm

24-hour clocks show time like this:

12-hour clock times use **am** or **pm** to show whether a time is before or after midday

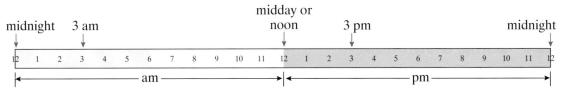

24-hour clock times number the hours from **0** to **23**

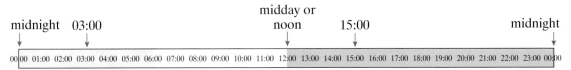

■ **The 24-hour clock always uses four digits.**
The first two digits show the hours.
The last two digits show the minutes.

■ **To change 12-hour times to 24-hour times:**

8.30 am → **08:30**	24-hour time always has 4 digits.
11.25 am → **11:25**	The minute digits stay the same.
2.57 pm → **14:57**	Add 12 to the number of hours pm.
12.35 am → **00:35**	Times between midnight and 1 am start with 00 in 24-hour time.

Exercise 7K

1 Write these times using the 24-hour clock

(a) 8:00 am   (b) 9:15 am   (c) 11:20 am

(d) 1:30 pm   (e) 3:45 pm   (f) 4:15 pm

(g) 9:15 pm   (h) 10:00 pm   (i) 11:15 pm

(j) midday   (k) midnight   (l) 12:25 am

2 Write these times using am or pm.
  (a) 11:00 **(b)** 14:40 **(c)** 17:15 **(d)** 08:10 **(e)** 03:50
  (f) 21:30 **(g)** 23:17 **(h)** 00:38 **(i)** 12:23 **(j)** 00:01

3 Write these times using the 24-hour clock:
  (a) Quarter past six in the morning
  (b) Half past two in the afternoon
  (c) Quarter to ten in the morning
  (d) Ten to six in the evening
  (e) Twenty-four minutes past six in the evening
  (f) Ten past midnight

7.10 Using a calendar

■ **There are 7 days in a week**
         52 weeks in a year
         12 months in a year.

This is the calendar for the year 2005.

January

M	T	W	T	F	S	S
					1	2
3	4	5	6	7	8	9
10	11	12	13	14	15	16
17	18	19	20	21	22	23
24	25	26	27	28	29	30
31						

February

M	T	W	T	F	S	S
	1	2	3	4	5	6
7	8	9	10	11	12	13
14	15	16	17	18	19	20
21	22	23	24	25	26	27
28						

March

M	T	W	T	F	S	S
	1	2	3	4	5	6
7	8	9	10	11	12	13
14	15	16	17	18	19	20
21	22	23	24	25	26	27
28	29	30	31			

April

M	T	W	T	F	S	S
				1	2	3
4	5	6	7	8	9	10
11	12	13	14	15	16	17
18	19	20	21	22	23	24
25	26	27	28	29	30	

May

M	T	W	T	F	S	S
						1
2	3	4	5	6	7	8
9	10	11	12	13	14	15
16	17	18	19	20	21	22
23	24	25	26	27	28	29
30	31					

June

M	T	W	T	F	S	S
		1	2	3	4	5
6	7	8	9	10	11	12
13	14	15	16	17	18	19
20	21	22	23	24	25	26
27	28	29	30			

July

M	T	W	T	F	S	S
				1	2	3
4	5	6	7	8	9	10
11	12	13	14	15	16	17
18	19	20	21	22	23	24
25	26	27	28	29	30	31

August

M	T	W	T	F	S	S
1	2	3	4	5	6	7
8	9	10	11	12	13	14
15	16	17	18	19	20	21
22	23	24	25	26	27	28
29	30	31				

September

M	T	W	T	F	S	S
			1	2	3	4
5	6	7	8	9	10	11
12	13	14	15	16	17	18
19	20	21	22	23	24	25
26	27	28	29	30		

October

M	T	W	T	F	S	S
					1	2
3	4	5	6	7	8	9
10	11	12	13	14	15	16
17	18	19	20	21	22	23
24	25	26	27	28	29	30
31						

November

M	T	W	T	F	S	S
	1	2	3	4	5	6
7	8	9	10	11	12	13
14	15	16	17	18	19	20
21	22	23	24	25	26	27
28	29	30				

December

M	T	W	T	F	S	S
			1	2	3	4
5	6	7	8	9	10	11
12	13	14	15	16	17	18
19	20	21	22	23	24	25
26	27	28	29	30	31	

Example 9

(a) On what day of the week is 18th November?

(b) How long is it from 18th November to Christmas Day?

November	December
M T W T F S S	M T W T F S S
1 2 3 4 5 6	1 2 3 4
7 8 9 10 11 12 13	5 6 7 8 9 10 11
14 15 16 17 (18) 19 20	12 13 14 15 16 17 18
21 22 23 24 25 26 27	19 20 21 22 23 24 25
28 29 30	26 27 28 29 30 31

(a) 18th November is a Friday. (18)

(b) Christmas Day is 25th December.

There are 5 weeks to 23rd December.

It is 5 weeks 2 days from 18th November to Christmas Day.

5 weeks
25 2 9 16 23

5 weeks and 2 days
25 2 9 16 23 24 25

Exercise 7L

Use the calendar for the year 2005 to answer the questions.

1 On what day of the week is each pupil's birthday?

Ray — 4th December
Sarah — 31st January
Michele — 7th May
Mandy — 26th September

2 Which dates in February are Saturdays?

3 What day of the week is:

(a) three days before March 2nd

(b) 7 days after June 7th

(c) 21 days after August 19th

(d) 7 days before November 28th?

4 What date is:

(a) 21 days after September 17th

(b) 14 days before April 2nd

(c) 15 days after May 24th

(d) 15 days before October 9th?

7.11 Using timetables

This is part of a timetable for trains from Morecambe to Southport. Each colour represents one train.

Morecambe	06:30	07:30	08:30
Lancaster	06:50	08:00	09:00
Preston	07:40	09:00	----
Southport	08:50	09:40	10:40

The third train leaves Morecambe at 08:30.

It arrives at Lancaster at 09:00.

It does not stop at Preston.

It arrives at Southport at 10:40.

Example 10

Using the timetable:

(a) At what time does the first train leave Morecambe?

(b) At what time does the 07:30 train from Morecambe arrive at Lancaster?

(c) Which is the latest train I could catch from Lancaster to get to Southport by 10:00?

(a) The first train leaves at 06:30. (The red train)

(b) The 07:30 train arrives in Lancaster at 0800. (The blue train)

(c) The 08:00 train from Lancaster arrives at Southport at 09:40. (The blue train)

Exercise 7M

1 Here is part of a train timetable.

London	07:30	08:00	08:30	09:00
Peterborough	----	08:45	09:20	09:45
Doncaster	09:00	----	10:15	----
York	09:25	09:50	10:40	10:50
Darlington	09:55	10:20	11:10	11:20
Newcastle	10:30	10:50	11:40	11:50

(a) How many trains are shown on the timetable?

(b) At what time does the 07:30 train from London arrive at York?

(c) At what time does the 09:45 train from Peterborough arrive at Darlington?

(d) When does the train that arrives in Darlington at 11:10 leave Doncaster?

(e) What is the latest train I could catch from York to get to Darlington by 11:00?

2 This is part of a boat's timetable.

Mallaig	05:00	06:00	10:30	12:30
Canna	07:30	08:30	14:45	17:00
Rum	08:30	09:30	----	----
Muck	09:45	----	----	----
Eigg	10:30	10:45	----	----

(a) At what time does the last boat leave Mallaig?

(b) What is the latest boat from Mallaig to Eigg?

(c) At which places does the 05:00 boat from Mallaig stop?

(d) What is the journey time from Canna to Rum?

3 Here is part of a rail timetable.

Bath Spa	07:50	08:50	09:51	10:35
Freshford	07:59	----	10:00	----
Avoncliff	08:01	----	10:02	----
Bradford-on-Avon	08:04	09:03	10:05	----
Trowbridge	08:10	09:09	10:11	10:50

(a) At which stations does the 08:50 from Bath Spa not stop?

(b) At what time does the 10:00 from Freshford arrive at Trowbridge?

(c) Which trains can you catch from Bath Spa if you are getting off at Avoncliff?

(d) You just miss the 07:50 train from Bath Spa. When does the next train leave for Avoncliff?

Summary of key points

1 $100\,\text{cm} = 1\,\text{m}$
    $200\,\text{cm} = 2\,\text{m}$
    $300\,\text{cm} = 3\,\text{m}$

centimetres (cm), metres (m) and kilometres (km) are used to measure distances.

2 $1000\,\text{m} = 1\,\text{km}$
    $2000\,\text{m} = 2\,\text{km}$

3 $1000\,\text{g} = 1\,\text{kg}$
    $1000\,\text{kg} = 1\,\text{t}$

grams (g), kilograms (kg) and tonnes (t) are used to measure weights.

4 An analogue clock has hands.
    A digital clock has a number display.

5 You use am for times before midday.
    You use pm for times after midday.

6 The 24 hour clock always uses four digits.
    The first two digits show the hours.
    The last two digits show the minutes.

7 To change 12 hour times to 24 hour times:

    $8.30\,\text{am} \rightarrow 08:30$ 24 hour time always has 4 digits
    $11.25\,\text{am} \rightarrow 11:25$ The minute digits stay the same.
    $2.57\,\text{pm} \rightarrow 14:57$ Add 12 to the number of hours pm.
    $12.35\,\text{am} \rightarrow 00:35$ Times between midnight and 1 am start with 00 in 24 hour time.

8 There are 7 days in a week
            52 weeks in a year
            12 months in a year.

8 Fractions

All these things are divided into equal parts called **fractions**:

This symbol has two halves.

One part is **one half** or $\frac{1}{2}$ of the symbol.

This swimming pool has four lanes.

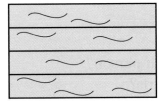

Each lane is **one quarter** or $\frac{1}{4}$ of the pool.

This pie has eight slices.

Each slice is **one eighth** or – of the pie.

8.1 Using numbers to represent fractions

Three quarters or $\frac{3}{4}$ of this garden is grass:

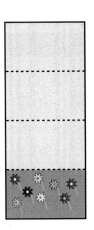

■ The top number shows 3 parts are grass.

The top number is the **numerator**.

$$\frac{3}{4}$$

The bottom number shows the garden has 4 equal parts.

The bottom number is the **denominator**.

Example 1

A quarter of the garden has flowers

(a) Write a quarter as a fraction.

(b) What is the numerator?

(c) What is the denominator?

(a) a quarter is $\frac{1}{4}$

(b) the numerator is 1.

(c) the denominator is 4.

When is a fraction not a fraction?

Each slice is the same size. Each slice is $\frac{1}{3}$ or **one third**.

These slices are unequal. They are **not** thirds.

Example 2

This pop group has 5 people in it: 2 boys and 3 girls.

(a) What fraction of the group is each person?
(b) What fraction of the group are girls?

(a) Each person is $\frac{1}{5}$ of the group.

(b) The girls are $\frac{3}{5}$ of the group.

Notice that 3 out of 5 are girls.
The fraction is $\frac{3}{5}$.

Exercise 8A

1 Write down the numerator of each fraction:
(a) $\frac{2}{3}$ **(b)** $\frac{4}{5}$ **(c)** $\frac{3}{4}$ **(d)** $\frac{7}{10}$ **(e)** $\frac{5}{7}$ **(f)** $\frac{12}{20}$

2 Write down the denominator of each fraction:
(a) $\frac{1}{2}$ **(b)** $\frac{3}{10}$ **(c)** $\frac{5}{6}$ **(d)** $\frac{3}{8}$ **(e)** $\frac{4}{7}$ **(f)** $\frac{13}{16}$

3 For each of the following shapes:
- write down the total number of parts (the denominator)
- write down the number of shaded parts (the numerator)
- what fraction of the shape is shaded?

(a) 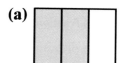 **(b)** 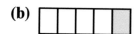 **(c)**

(d)   **(e)** 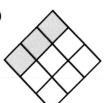 **(f)**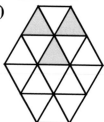

4 What fraction of each flag is red?

(a)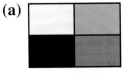

(b)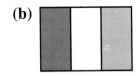

(c)

(d)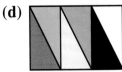

(e)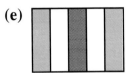

(f)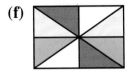

5 This crossword has 25 squares.

(a) What fraction is one square?

(b) What fraction is shaded?

(c) What fraction is not shaded?

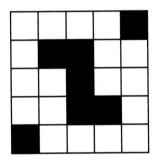

6 Sheila and Paul buy a six pack of yoghurt.
Sheila likes only strawberry yoghurt. Paul does not like strawberry but he likes the others.

(a) What fraction of the pack does Sheila like?

(b) What fraction of the pack does Paul like?

8.2 Fractions in words

You can write fractions in words.

$\frac{1}{5}$ is one fifth $\frac{2}{5}$ is two fifths $\frac{3}{5}$ is three fifths

The name *fifths* is like a family name. It comes from the denominator (bottom).

Remember: the denominator shows the number of equal parts there are.

A few fraction families have special names:

Two equal parts $\frac{1}{2}$ is **one half.**

Three equal parts $\frac{1}{3}$ is **one third.**

Four equal parts $\frac{1}{4}$ is **one quarter.**

Five equal parts $\frac{1}{5}$ is **one fifth.**

The rest of the fraction families are made in the same way:

Six parts gives **six**ths $\frac{1}{6}$

Seven parts gives **seven**ths $\frac{1}{7}$

Eight parts gives **eight**ths $\frac{1}{8}$

Nine parts gives **nin**ths $\frac{1}{9}$

Ten parts gives **ten**ths $\frac{1}{10}$

■ **Fraction family names come from the number on the bottom: the denominator.**

Example 3

What fraction of this shape is blue?
Give your answer using:

(a) numbers

(b) words

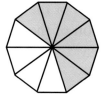

The shape has 10 equal parts so the denominator is 10.

6 parts are shaded so the numerator is 6.

The fraction is:

(a) $\frac{6}{10}$

(b) six tenths

Example 4

Write $\frac{3}{7}$ in words.

The denominator is 7 so the family name is sevenths.

$\frac{3}{7}$ is three sevenths.

Example 5

Write four fifths using numbers.

The family name is fifths so the denominator is 5.

Four fifths is $\frac{4}{5}$.

Exercise 8B

1 Write these fractions in words:

    (a) $\frac{1}{3}$ **(b)** $\frac{2}{3}$ **(c)** $\frac{3}{5}$ **(d)** $\frac{1}{10}$ **(e)** $\frac{5}{6}$ **(f)** $\frac{3}{4}$ **(g)** $\frac{5}{7}$ **(h)** $\frac{3}{8}$

2 Write these fractions as numbers:

    (a) three quarters **(b)** one half **(c)** two fifths

    (d) three tenths **(e)** five eighths **(f)** one sixth

3 What fraction of each shape is coloured?
Give your answers in words and using numbers.

    (a) 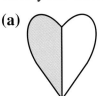 **(b)**  **(c)**   **(d)**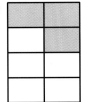

4 Here are two ways of shading one quarter of a square. Find three other ways to shade one quarter of a square.

5 Morgan, Fred and Cassie each buy a chocolate bar. They break their bars into equal parts.
Copy and complete the sentences with words:

    (a) Morgan broke his bar in two, so each part was a ...

    (b) Fred broke his bar in four so each part was a ...

    (c) Cassie made six pieces so each part was a ...

6 Amas shared her raisins with Mark so they both received the same amount. What fraction did they each receive? Give your answer in words.

7 There are twelve cats at Moppet pet home. Four cats are tabbies, five are ginger and three are Siamese. What fraction of the cats are tabbies? Write your answer in words and in numbers.

> Hint: twelve equal parts gives twelfths.

8 In the school library there are one thousand books. Four hundred and sixty are fiction books.

(a) What fraction of the books are fiction?

(b) What fraction of the books are not fiction?

8.3 Finding fractions

Sometimes you need to find a fraction of a quantity.

■ **A half means one of two shares. To find half of a number you divide it by 2.**

■ **A third means one of three shares. To find a third of a number you divide it by 3.**

■ **A quarter means one of four shares. To find a quarter of a number you divide it by 4.**

Example 6

Find $\frac{1}{4}$ of 12.

$\frac{1}{4}$ means one of 4 shares.

$12 \div 4 = 3$

so $\frac{1}{4}$ of 12 is 3

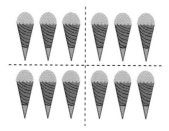

> $12 \div 4$ means 12 divided by 4
>
> There is more about dividing on page 77

Example 7

Find $\frac{1}{3}$ of 18.

$\frac{1}{3}$ means one of three shares.

$18 \div 3 = 6$

so $\frac{1}{3}$ of 18 is 6

Example 8

Find $\frac{1}{2}$ of 30p.

$\frac{1}{2}$ means one of two shares.

$$30p \div 2 = 15p$$

so $\frac{1}{2}$ of 30p is 15p.

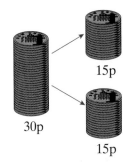

15p

30p

15p

Exercise 8C

1 Find:
   (a) $\frac{1}{2}$ of 14   (b) $\frac{1}{3}$ of 27   (c) $\frac{1}{10}$ of 80   (d) $\frac{1}{5}$ of 40

2 Find:
   (a) $\frac{1}{3}$ of 15 biscuits   (b) $\frac{1}{5}$ of £30   (c) $\frac{1}{4}$ of 16 kg
   (d) $\frac{1}{2}$ of 32 hours   (e) $\frac{1}{10}$ of 60p

3 $\frac{1}{4}$ of Julian's journey home from school is by bus.
   He lives 8 km from the school. How far does he travel
   by bus?

4 The school cafeteria sold 150 cartons
   of drink at morning break.
   $\frac{1}{3}$ of these were orange juice. $\frac{1}{10}$ were pineapple juice.
   (a) How many were orange?
   (b) How many were pineapple?

5 Nigel has 30 lessons each week.
   $\frac{1}{6}$ of these lessons are Maths. $\frac{1}{5}$ of his lessons are English.
   (a) How many Maths lessons does he have each
       week?
   (b) How many English lessons does he have each
       week?

6 Nuala had £5.00 of her pocket money left. She needed
   to keep $\frac{1}{5}$ of it for her magazine. How much did the
   magazine cost?

7 The librarian said that $\frac{1}{10}$ of her 80 fairy tale books had
   not been returned to the school. How many of these
   books had been returned?

8.4 Comparing fractions

Rob and Hayley are walking along the corridor:

Hayley is $\frac{1}{3}$ of the way along.

Rob is $\frac{1}{4}$ of the way along.

Notice that $\frac{1}{3}$ is more than $\frac{1}{4}$

but 3 is less than 4

■ **The bigger the denominator (bottom) ...**
... the more parts in the fraction
... the smaller each part is.

Example 9

Mary has $\frac{1}{3}$ of a bar of nougat, Keith has $\frac{1}{6}$ of the same bar.

For each sentence, write **true** or **false**.

(a) Mary has more nougat than Keith.

(b) Keith has more nougat than Mary.

(c) They have the same amount of nougat.

$\frac{1}{3}$ means one of three shares.

6 parts $\div 3 = 2$

Mary gets two parts.

$\frac{1}{6}$ means one of six shares.

6 parts $\div 6 = 1$

Keith gets 1 part.

(a) True   **(b)** False   **(c)** False

Notice that
$\frac{1}{3}$ is more than $\frac{1}{6}$
but 3 is less than 6.

Exercise 8D

1   Jack and Jill are running a 100 m race. Jack has run $\frac{1}{10}$
    of the way and Jill has run $\frac{1}{5}$ of the way.
    Who has run the furthest?

2   Diana and Gina are tiling their bathroom. They have a
    box of 50 tiles. Gina uses $\frac{1}{2}$ of the tiles and Diana uses $\frac{1}{5}$
    of the tiles. Who uses the most tiles?

3   Amy, Mary and Tom have won £90 on the lottery. Amy
    gets one ninth, Mary gets one fifth and Tom gets the
    rest.
    Who gets the most money?

4   Draw a number line like this:

    $0 \longrightarrow 1$

    Start from the left and:
    (a) Put a mark $\frac{1}{2}$ of the way along the line.
    (b) Put a mark $\frac{1}{3}$ of the way along the line.
    (c) Put a mark $\frac{1}{4}$ of the way along the line.
    (d) Put a mark $\frac{1}{5}$ of the way along the line.
    (e) Put the fractions $\frac{1}{2}, \frac{1}{3}, \frac{1}{4}$ and $\frac{1}{5}$ in order of size.
        Start with the smallest.

8.5 Adding fractions

You can add fractions together. This is easy if they belong
to the same fraction family.

How to add fractions with the same denominator

$$\frac{1}{3} + \frac{1}{3} = \frac{2}{3}$$

Add the numerators (top).

Write them over the **same**
denominator (bottom).

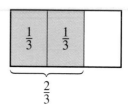

The fraction family is thirds.

■ **To add fractions with the same denominator add the
numerators. Write the result over the same
denominator.**

Example 10

$$\frac{1}{4} + \frac{2}{4} = \frac{3}{4}$$

Example 11

$$\frac{2}{8} + \frac{3}{8} = \frac{5}{8}$$

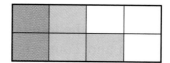

Exercise 8E

1 Add these fractions.

    (a) $\frac{1}{5} + \frac{2}{5}$ **(b)** $\frac{3}{10} + \frac{1}{10}$ **(c)** $\frac{2}{9} + \frac{5}{9}$ **(d)** $\frac{1}{3} + \frac{2}{3}$

    (e) What do you notice about part (d)?

2 Work out:

    (a) $\frac{1}{8} + \frac{4}{8}$ **(b)** $\frac{6}{10} + \frac{2}{10}$ **(c)** $\frac{4}{7} + \frac{2}{7}$

    (d) $\frac{8}{13} + \frac{2}{13}$ **(e)** $\frac{7}{20} + \frac{6}{20}$ **(f)** $\frac{4}{15} + \frac{9}{15}$

    (g) $\frac{7}{40} + \frac{15}{40}$ **(h)** $\frac{1}{50} + \frac{18}{50}$ **(i)** $\frac{11}{100} + \frac{40}{100}$

    (j) $\frac{1}{8} + \frac{2}{8} + \frac{1}{8}$ **(k)** $\frac{2}{5} + \frac{1}{5} + \frac{1}{5}$ **(l)** $\frac{6}{10} + \frac{1}{10} + \frac{2}{10}$

    (m) $\frac{1}{20} + \frac{6}{20} + \frac{7}{20}$ **(n)** $\frac{1}{4} + \frac{2}{4} + \frac{1}{4}$ **(o)** $\frac{3}{4} + \frac{2}{4} + \frac{1}{4}$

Summary of key points

1 You can use numbers to represent a fraction:

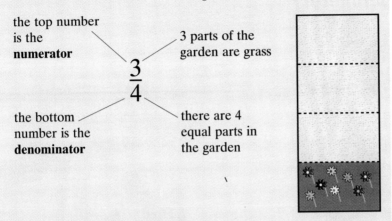

the top number is the **numerator**

3 parts of the garden are grass

$\dfrac{3}{4}$

the bottom number is the **denominator**

there are 4 equal parts in the garden

2 Fraction family names come from the number on the bottom of the fraction, the denominator.

3 A half means one of two shares. To find half of a number you divide it by 2.

4 A third means one of three shares. To find a third of a number you divide it by 3.

5 A quarter means one of four shares. To find a quarter of a number you divide it by 4.

6 The bigger the denominator (bottom) ...
... the more parts in the fraction
... the smaller each part is.

7 To add fractions with the same denominator add the numerators. Write the result over the same denominator.

9 Perimeter, area and volume

9.1 What is a perimeter?

Naomi wants a frame for her new picture.
She measures the distance around the picture.
Now she knows how much wood to buy.

Peter is building a fence around his garden.
He measures the distance around the garden.
Now he knows how much fencing he needs.

■   **The distance around the edge of a shape is its perimeter.**

Example 1

Which shape has

(a) the longest perimeter

(b) the shortest perimeter?

Shape A looks like it has the longest perimeter.
Shape C looks like it has the shortest perimeter.

You can check using string:

A ——————————
B ——————————
C ——————

Shape A uses the most string.

Shape C uses the least string.

(a) Shape A has the longest perimeter.

(b) Shape C has the shortest perimeter.

Exercise 9A

1 Which shape has
  (a) the longest perimeter
  (b) the shortest perimeter?

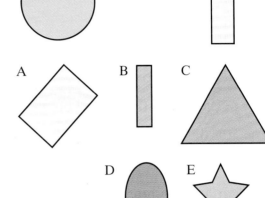

2 Which shape has
  (a) the longest perimeter
  (b) the shortest perimeter?
  (c) Put the shapes in order of perimeter size.

    Start with the shortest.

3 Put these shapes in order of perimeter size.
Start with the shortest perimeter.

Football pitch   The top of your table or desk
Tennis court   The floor of the room you are in
A page of this book

9.2 Measuring up

A perimeter is a measure of distance.

You use centimetres, metres or kilometres to measure distance.

Remember what these measures look like. Look back at page **101** to check.

You measure the perimeter of a card in centimetres.

You measure the perimeter of a room in metres.

You measure the perimeter of this lake in kilometres.

Exercise 9B

Which units would you use to measure these perimeters?
Write cm, m or km.

1 A leaf

2 A tennis court

3 A page of this book

4 The perimeter of the room you are in

5 The coastline of Ireland

6 A football pitch

7 The garden of a house

8 The thickness of this book

9.3 Counting the squares

This shape is drawn on centimetre squared paper.

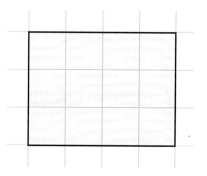

You can count the sides of the squares around the edge to find the perimeter.

Or you can add the lengths together to find the perimeter.

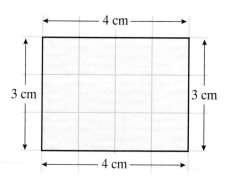

Perimeter = 14 cm

Perimeter = 4 + 3 + 4 + 3
= 14 cm

Sometimes you need to use a ruler to find a length.

Example 2

Find the perimeter of this shape:

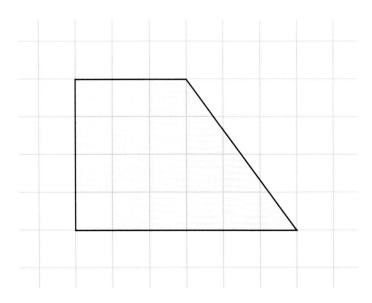

You need to measure the slanted line to find the length:

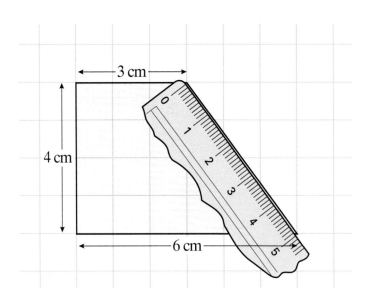

Remember to start from 0 on your ruler.

So the perimeter is $3 + 4 + 6 + 5 = 18$ cm.

Exercise 9C

1 These shapes are drawn on centimetre squared paper.
Find the perimeter of each shape.

2 Work out the perimeters of these shapes.
Remember to measure the slanted side.

(a)

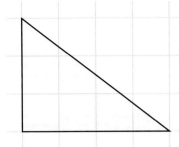

(b)

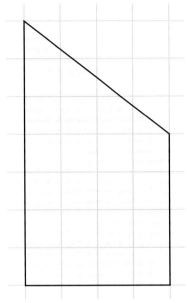

(c)

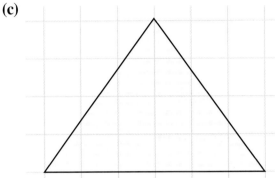

9.4 Adding it up

Kate is designing a kitchen.
The builders need to know how
much skirting board to order.
She gives them this plan:

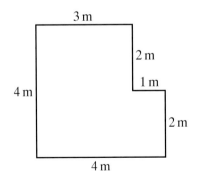

The builders add the lengths together to find the perimeter:

perimeter $= 3 + 2 + 1 + 2 + 4 + 4 = 16$ m

Now they know how much skirting board they need.

■ **You can find the perimeter of a shape by adding the lengths of its edges.**

Example 3

Find the perimeter of:

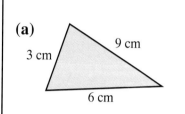

(a)

3 cm

9 cm

6 cm

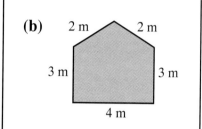

(b)

2 m   2 m

3 m   3 m

4 m

Hint: To make sure you add all the lengths, count the number of sides first.

3 sides means you add 3 lengths.

5 sides means you add 5 lengths.

(a) Add the lengths

$3 + 9 + 6 = 18$

Perimeter $= 18\,\text{cm}$

Remember to put the units in your answer.

(b) Add the lengths

$2 + 2 + 3 + 4 + 3 = 14$

Perimeter $= 14\,\text{m}$

Exercise 9D

The shapes in this exercise are *not* accurately drawn.

Find the perimeter by adding the lengths:

1

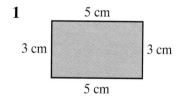

5 cm

3 cm   3 cm

5 cm

2

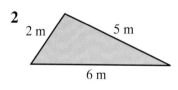

2 m   5 m

6 m

3

4 cm   4 cm

4 cm   4 cm

4 cm

4

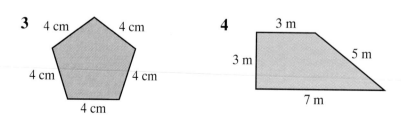

3 m

3 m   5 m

7 m

5

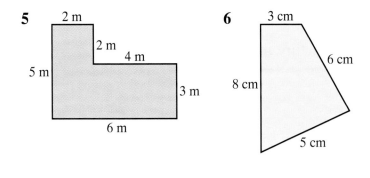

6

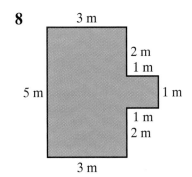

7

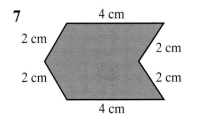

8

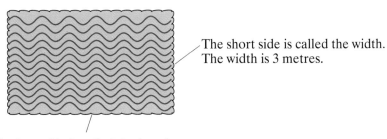

9.5 Perimeter of a rectangle

This rug is a rectangle:

When you measure a rectangle . . .

The short side is called the width.
The width is 3 metres.

The long side is called the length.
The length is 5 metres.

The rug measures 3 metres by 5 metres.

You could also write:

The rug is a rectangle with sides 3 metres and 5 metres.

Example 4

Find the perimeter of a rectangular picture measuring 20 cm by 15 cm.

First sketch the shape:

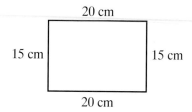

Add the lengths together:

$$15 + 20 + 15 + 20 = 70$$

Give the units in your answer:
The perimeter is 70 cm.

Exercise 9E

1 Work out the perimeter of this carpet.

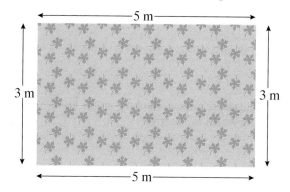

2 Work out the perimeters of these shapes:

(a) A carpet measuring 5 m by 4 m.

(b) A rectangular field measuring 300 m by 200 m.

(c) A rectangular playground measuring 45 m by 35 m.

(d) A rectangular envelope measuring 20 cm by 10 cm.

(e) A tennis court measuring 11 m by 24 m.

(f) A square with each side measuring 10 cm.

9.6 Area

Ahmed needs to know what size carpet to buy for his front room.

Jim wants to know how much paint to buy to cover the walls.

Holly wants to know what size glass to buy to mend a window.

Ahmed, Jim and Holly each need to measure an **area**.

■ **Area is the amount of space covered by a shape.**

Example 5

Which of these shapes has:

(a) the largest area

(b) the smallest area?

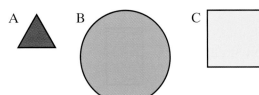

A   B   C

Look at how much space each shape covers.

Shape B covers the most.
Shape A covers the least.

(a) Shape B has the largest area.

(b) Shape A has the smallest area.

Exercise 9F

1   Which of these shapes has

(a) the largest area

(b) the smallest area?

A   B   C

2 Which of these shapes has:

(a) the smallest area

(b) the largest area?

(c) Put the shapes in order of area size.

Start with the smallest area.

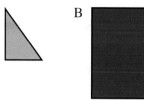

3 Put these shapes in order of area size.
Start with the smallest area.

Football pitch   The top of your table or desk

Tennis court   The floor of the room you are in

A page of this book

9.7 Using squares

■ **You can use squares to measure area.**

These shapes are drawn on squared paper:

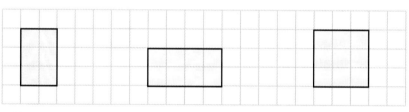

This shape covers 6 squares. The area is 6 squares.

This shape covers 8 squares. The area is 8 squares.

This shape covers 9 squares. The area is 9 squares.

These shapes are drawn on centimetre squared paper.
Each square measures 1 cm by 1 cm.

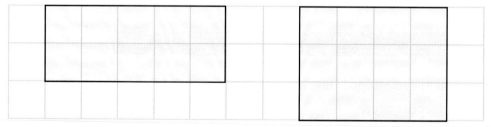

This shape covers 10 centimetre squares.
The area is 10 square centimetres.
You can write this: 10 sq cm or 10 cm^2.

This shape covers 12 centimetre squares.
The area is 12 square centimetres.
You can write this: 12 sq cm or 12 cm^2.

■ **You can measure area in square centimetres.**
You find the number of centimetre squares the shape
covers.

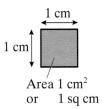

1 cm

1 cm

Area 1 cm²
or   1 sq cm

Exercise 9G

The shapes in this exercise are all drawn on centimetre
squared paper.

Write down the area of each shape.

1 **(a)**   **(b)**

(c)   **(d)**

(e)   **(f)**

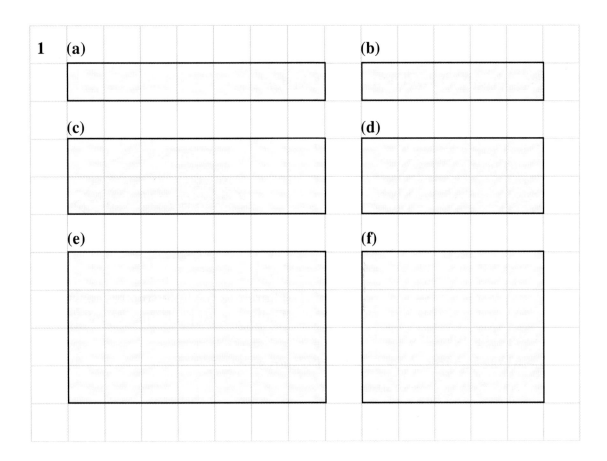

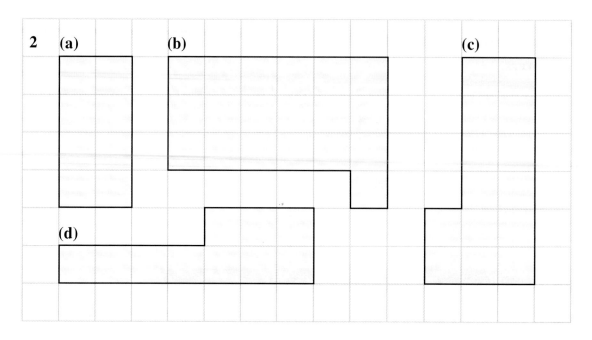

9.8 Estimating areas

To find the area of a curved shape you need to estimate the
number of squares it covers.

Example 6

This leaf is drawn on centimetre squared paper.

Estimate the area of the leaf:

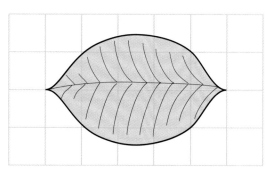

Count the whole squares first:

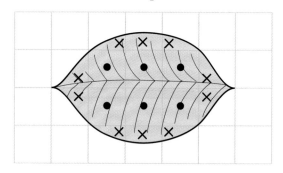

There are 6 whole squares marked ●
There are 10 part squares marked ✕

A good estimate for the area is:

The whole squares + half the part squares.

6   + half of 10

6   + 5 = 11

The area of the leaf is about 11 sq cm.

■ **To estimate the area of a curved shape** ...
First count the whole squares.
Then count each part square as half a whole square.

The shapes in this exercise are drawn on centimetre
squared paper.

1 Estimate the area of this shape:

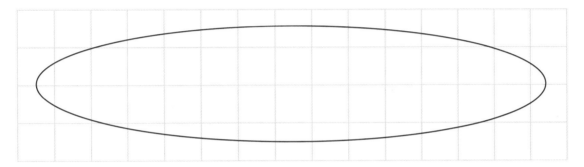

2 Estimate the area of each leaf:

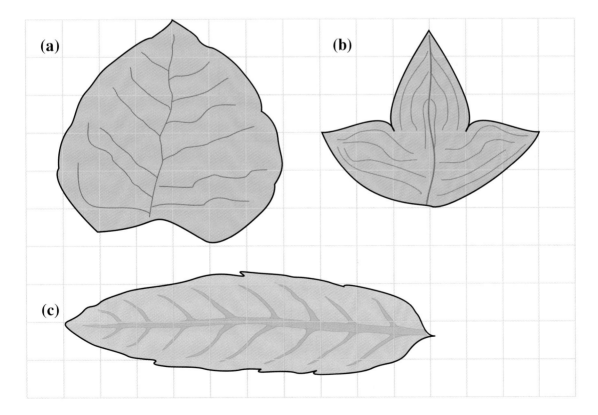

(a)

(b)

(c)

3 Put your hand on a piece of centimetre squared paper.

Draw round it.

Estimate the area of your hand.

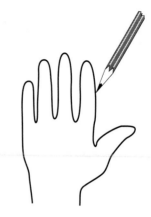

9.9 Areas by multiplying

It can take a long time to count squares.

Sometimes it is quicker to use multiplication.

This rectangle measures 2 cm by 3 cm.

	1	2	3
	4	5	6

By counting the squares:
The area is 6 sq cm.

There are 2 rows of 3 cm squares.

1	2	3
1	2	3

sq is short for square

By multiplying:
The area is $2 \times 3 = 6$ sq cm.

Example 7

Find the area of the rectangle.

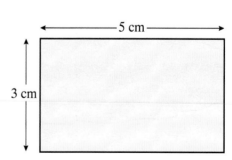

Imagine it split into rows:

There are 3 rows

There are 5 sq cm in each row

So the area is $3 \times 5 = 15$ sq cm.

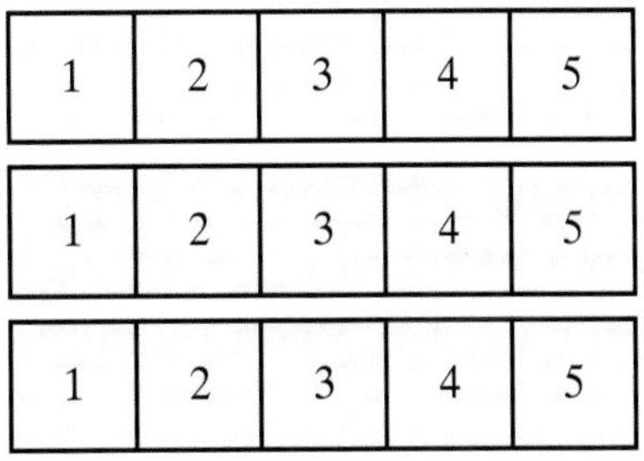

1	2	3	4	5
1	2	3	4	5
1	2	3	4	5

Exercise 9I

1 These rectangles have been split into rows.
   For each rectangle:

- How many rows are there?
- How many centimetre squares are there in each row?
- Multiply to find the area.

(a)

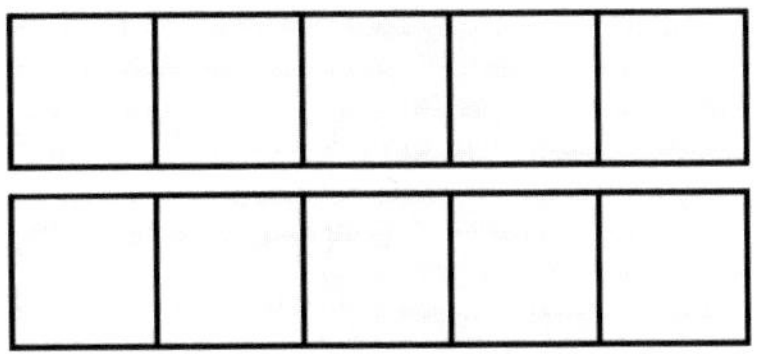

(b)

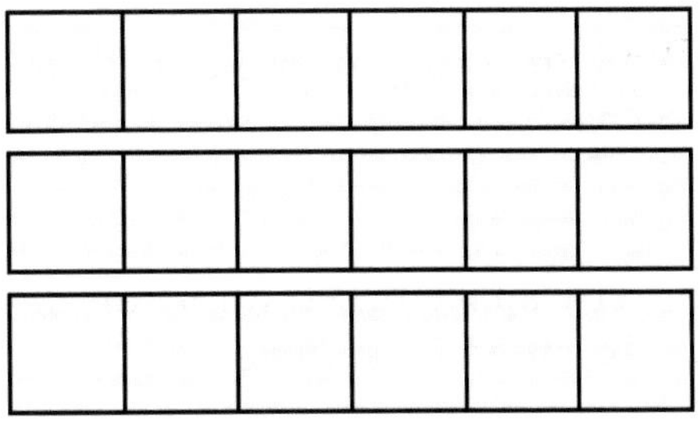

(c)

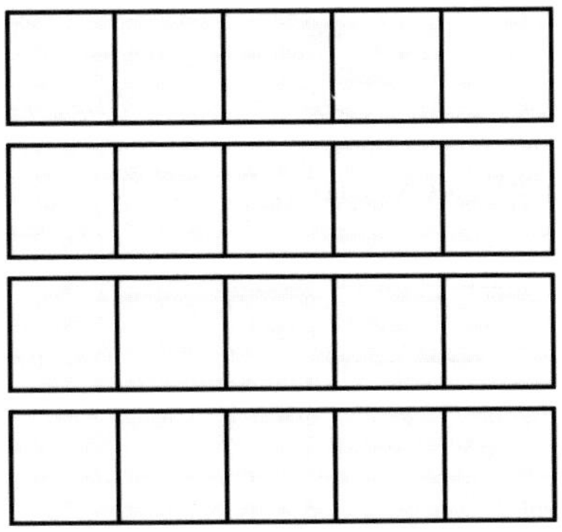

(d)

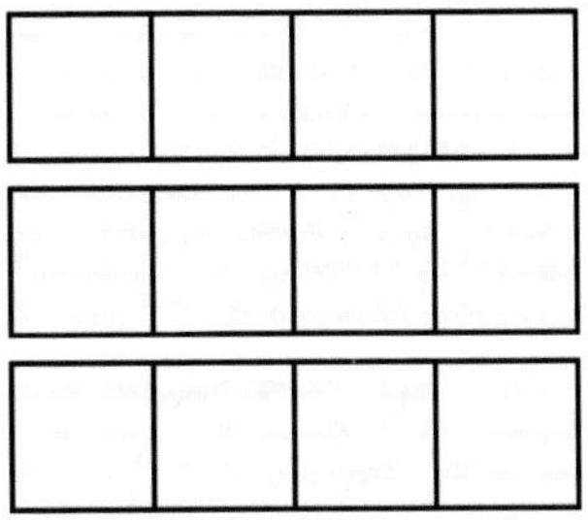

2 These rectangles were drawn on centimetre squared paper.

- How many rows were there?
- How many centimetre squares were there in a row?
- Find the area of each rectangle.

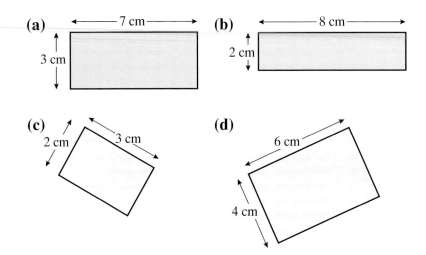

9.10 Volume

Bob wants to know what size washing machine will fit in his kitchen.

He needs to buy one that will fit in the space.

■ **The space taken up by an object is called its *volume*.**

Example 8

Which of these objects has:

(a) the largest volume **(b)** the smallest volume?

  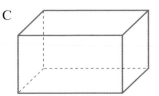

Look at how much space each object takes up.

C takes up the most space.
A takes up the least space.

Hint: imagine you put each object in your bag. Which one would take up most room?

(a) C has the largest volume.
(b) A has the smallest volume.

Exercise 9J

1 Which of these objects has:
 (a) the largest volume
 (b) the smallest volume?

A B 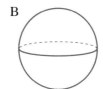 C

2 Which of these objects has:
 (a) the smallest volume
 (b) the largest volume?

A B C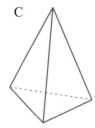

3 Put these objects in order of size.
 Start with the smallest volume.

 Football   Hot air balloon   Tennis ball   Marble

4 These four objects can hold liquid.
 Teacup   Teaspoon   Washing up bowl   Milk carton
 (a) Which one holds most liquid?
 (b) Put them in order starting with the one that can
   hold the most liquid.

9.11 Counting cubes

■ **You can use cubes to measure volume.**

You can measure volumes using
centimetre cubes.

Just count the number of cubes.

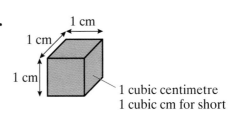

1 cm

1 cm

1 cm

1 cubic centimetre
1 cubic cm for short

Example 9

These shapes are made from centimetre cubes.

Find the volume of each shape:

(a) 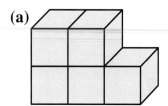   **(b)**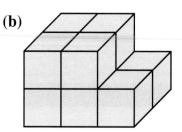

(a) There are 5 centimetre cubes.
The volume is
5 cubic centimetres.
(5 cubic cm for short)

(b) This shape is 2 cubes deep.
The front part has 5 cubes
The back part has 5 cubes
$5 + 5 = 10$ cubic cm.

Exercise 9K

All the shapes in this exercise are made from centimetre cubes.

Work out the volumes of the shapes.

1 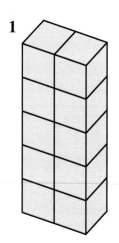   **2** 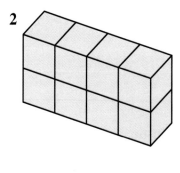   **3**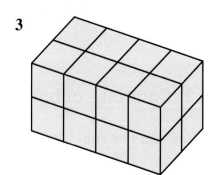

4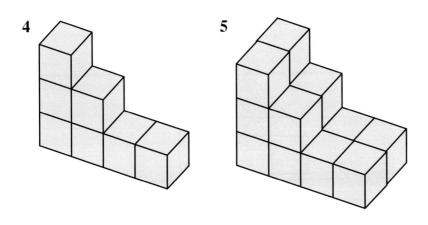

5

6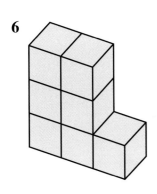

7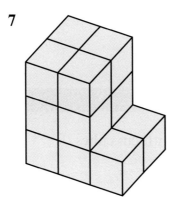

9.12 Volume of a cuboid

This shape is a cuboid:

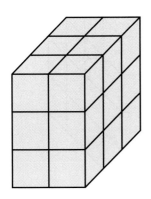

Remember:
A cuboid is a solid
shape with
rectangular faces.

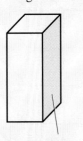

Each side
is a face

You can find the volume of a cuboid by counting the cubes in each layer.

The top layer has $3 \times 2 = 6$ cubes

There are 3 layers.

Each has 6 cubes.

$3 \times 6 = 18$

The volume is 18 cubic cm.

top layer

middle layer

bottom layer

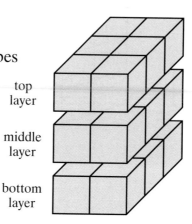

Hint:
cubic cm is another way of writing cubic centimetres.

Exercise 9L

All these cuboids are made with cm cubes.

For each cuboid write down:

(a) the number of cubes in the top layer

(b) the number of layers

(c) the volume of the cuboid.

1

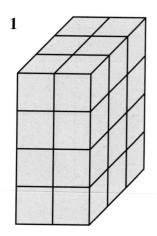

2

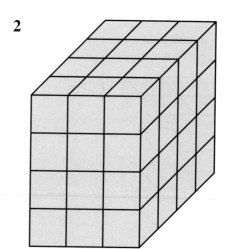

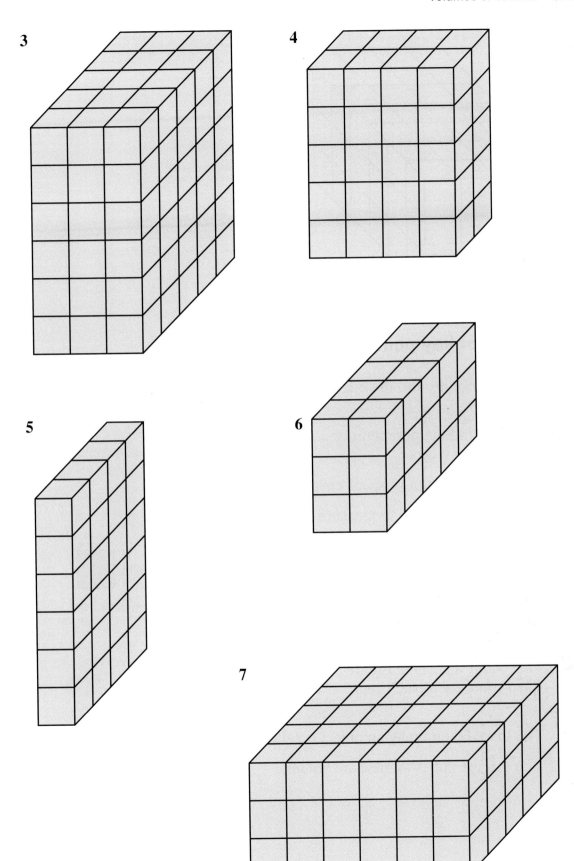

3

4

5

6

7

8

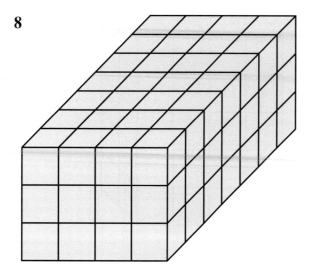

Summary of key points

1   The distance around the edge of a shape is its perimeter.

2   You can find the perimeter of a shape by adding the lengths of its edges.

3   Area is the amount of space covered by a shape.

4   You can use squares to measure area.

5   You can measure area in square centimetres. You find the number of centimetre squares the shape covers.

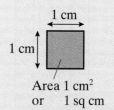

Area 1 cm²
or   1 sq cm

6   To estimate the area of a curved shape …
First count the whole squares.
Then count each part square as half a whole square.

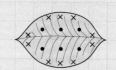

7   The space taken up by an object is called its **volume**.

8   You can use cubes to measure volume.

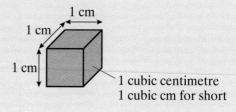

1 cubic centimetre
1 cubic cm for short

10 Formulae and equations

This unit shows you how to use formulae and equations to help solve problems.

Formulae is the plural of formula.

10.1 Using word formulae

- **A formula is a sentence describing a rule or a relationship.**
  It must contain an equals (=) sign.

Example 1

Helen buys cakes from a shop. This formula describes the total cost:

cost of cakes = cost of one cake × number of cakes bought

One cake costs 20p. If Helen buys 4 cakes how much do they cost altogether?

Put the numbers into the word formula:

cost of cakes = cost of one cake × number of cakes bought
= 20p × 4
= 80p

Exercise 10A

1 Andrew buys some pencils. He uses the formula:

cost of pencils = cost of one pencil × number of pencils bought

The cost of one pencil is 15p. Andrew buys 2 pencils.
Work out the total cost of the pencils.

2 Diana buys some buns. She uses the formula:

cost of buns = cost of one bun × number of buns bought

The cost of one bun is 24p. Diana buys 2 buns. Find the total cost of the buns.

3 Narinder buys some sweets. She uses the formula:

cost of sweets = cost of one sweet × number of sweets bought

The cost of one sweet is 5p. Narinder buys 6 sweets.
Work out the total cost of the sweets.

4 Sam buys some choc bars. He uses this formula:

cost of choc bars = cost of one choc bar × number of choc bars bought

The cost of one choc bar is 15p. Sam buys 3 choc bars.
Find the total cost of the choc bars.

5 Jo buys some apples. She uses the formula:

cost of apples = cost of one apple × number of apples bought

The cost of one apple is 12p. Jo buys 5 apples.
Find the total cost of the apples.

6 Thelma uses this formula to find the cost of some books:

cost of books = cost of one book × number of books bought

One book costs £3. Work out the total cost of 5 books.

7 Louise uses this formula to find the cost of some tapes.

cost of tapes = cost of one tape × number of tapes bought

One tape costs £5. Find the cost of 7 tapes.

8 Mohamed uses this formula to find the cost of some CDs.

cost of CDs = cost of one CD × number of CDs bought

One CD costs £10. Find the cost of 8 CDs.

9 Leon uses this formula to find the cost of cans of cola.

cost of cans = cost of one can × number of cans bought

One can of cola costs 30 pence. Work out the cost of 7
cans of cola.

10 Mario uses this formula to find the cost of some tapes:

cost of tapes = cost of one tape × number of tapes bought

One tape costs £5. Find the cost of 7 tapes.

11 Richard uses this formula to find the cost of some
pencils:

cost of pencils = cost of one pencil × number of pencils bought

One pencil costs 15p. Work out the cost of 8 pencils.

10.2 Writing word formulae

Sometimes you will need to write your own word formulae.
Remember that a formula always contains an equals sign.

Example 2

Write a word formula for the cost of chocolate bars. Use it
to find the cost of 3 chocolate bars at 35p each.

The formula you need is:

$$
\begin{aligned}
\text{cost of chocolate bars} &= \text{cost of one bar} \times \text{number of bars bought} \\
&= \quad\quad 35\text{p} \quad\quad \times \quad\quad 3 \\
&= 105\text{p} \\
&= \pounds1.05
\end{aligned}
$$

Exercise 10B

1 Write a word formula to find the cost of apples.
  Use it to find the cost of 4 apples at 25p each.

2 Write a word formula to find the cost of cans of orange
  drink.
  Use it to find the cost of 3 cans at 45p each.

3 Write a word formula to find the cost of chocolate bars.
  Use it to find the cost of 2 bars at 35p each.

4 Write a word formula to find the cost of buns.
  Use it to find the cost of 4 buns at 25p each.

5 Write a word formula to find the cost of apples.
  Use it to find the cost of 3 apples at 20p each.

6 Write a word formula to find the cost of peaches.
  Use it to find the cost of 3 peaches at 30p each.

7 Write a word formula to find the cost of kiwi fruit.
  Use it to find the cost of 4 kiwi fruit at 15p each.

8 Write a word formula to find the cost of cans of beans.
  Use it to find the cost of 4 cans of beans at 21p each.

9 Write a word formula to find the cost of packets of
  cereal.
  Use it to find the cost of 2 packets of cereal at 80p
  each.

10 Write a word formula to find the cost of jars of coffee.
    Use it to find the cost of 3 jars of coffee at £2 each.

11 Write a word formula to find the cost of cups of tea.
    Use it to find the cost of 4 cups at 60p each.

12 Write a word formula to find the cost of ice creams.
    Use it to find the cost of 5 ice creams at £1 each.

13 Write a word formula to find the cost of pencils.
    Use it to find the cost of 10 pencils at 15p each.

10.3 Using equations

■ **Equations and formulae are different:**

Equation	**Formula**
$2 + \boxed{} = 8$	$\text{cost} = \text{price} \times \text{number bought}$
This **equation** is **only true** when 6 is in the box. 6 is a solution to the equation	You can put **any values** into these parts of the **formula** and get a result for the cost.

An equation is a balancing act:

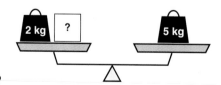

To balance the scales there must be the same amount on each side.

Example 3

These scales balance:

What must be in the box?

To balance the scales there must be 5 kg on each side.

3 kg must be in the box.

Exercise 10C

These scales all balance.

Find what must be in each box.

1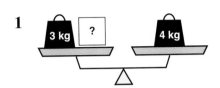

2

3

4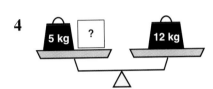

5

6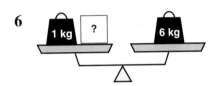

7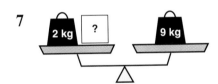

8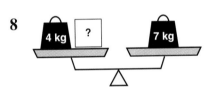

9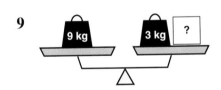

10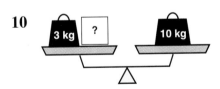

10.4 Solving equations

Here is a simple equation:

$$2 + \boxed{} = 7.$$

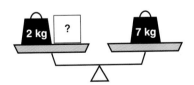

To make each side balance
5 must be in the box.

Finding the missing number is called
solving the equation.

5 is the **solution** to the equation.

Example 4

Solve these equations:

(a) $3 \times \boxed{} = 15$

(b) $\boxed{} \div 6 = 2$

(a) $3 \times 5 = 15$

so $\boxed{} = 5$

(b) $12 \div 6 = 2$

so $\boxed{} = 12$

Remember
The equals sign shows where the balance is. The missing number makes both sides the same.

■ **To solve an equation find the missing amount that makes it balance.**

Exercise 10D

Solve these equations:

1 $3 + \boxed{} = 7$

2 $2 + \boxed{} = 5$

3 $2 + \boxed{} = 6$

4 $1 + \boxed{} = 4$

5 $6 - \boxed{} = 2$

6 $6 - \boxed{} = 4$

7 $7 - \boxed{} = 2$

8 $5 - \boxed{} = 3$

9 $\boxed{} + 5 = 8$

10 $\boxed{} + 5 = 7$

11 $\boxed{} + 4 = 8$

12 $\boxed{} + 3 = 10$

13 $\boxed{} - 5 = 3$

14 $\boxed{} - 2 = 3$

15 $\boxed{} - 4 = 2$

16 $\boxed{} - 2 = 5$

17 $3 \times \boxed{} = 6$

18 $2 \times \boxed{} = 8$

19 $3 \times \boxed{} = 12$

20 $5 \times \boxed{} = 15$

21 $\boxed{} \times 2 = 8$

22 $\boxed{} \times 2 = 8$

23 $\boxed{} \times 4 = 12$

24 $\boxed{} \times 3 = 21$

25 $12 \div \boxed{} = 6$

26 $12 \div \boxed{} = 4$

27 $8 \div \boxed{} = 2$

28 $9 \div \boxed{} = 3$

29 $\boxed{} \div 2 = 4$

30 $\boxed{} \div 3 = 4$

31 $\boxed{} \div 3 = 6$

32 $\boxed{} \div 5 = 4$

Summary of key points

1   A formula is a sentence describing a rule or relationship.
     It must contain an equals (=) sign.

2   Equations and formulae are different:

Equation

$$2 + \boxed{} = 8$$

This **equation** is **only true** when 6 is in the box.
6 is a solution to the equation

Formula

$$\text{cost} = \text{price} \times \text{number bought}$$

You can put **any values** into these parts of the **formula** and get a result for the cost.

---

3   To solve an equation find the missing amount that makes it balance.

11 Positive and negative numbers

11.1 Measuring temperatures

This thermometer measures temperatures in degrees
Celsius, written °C for short.

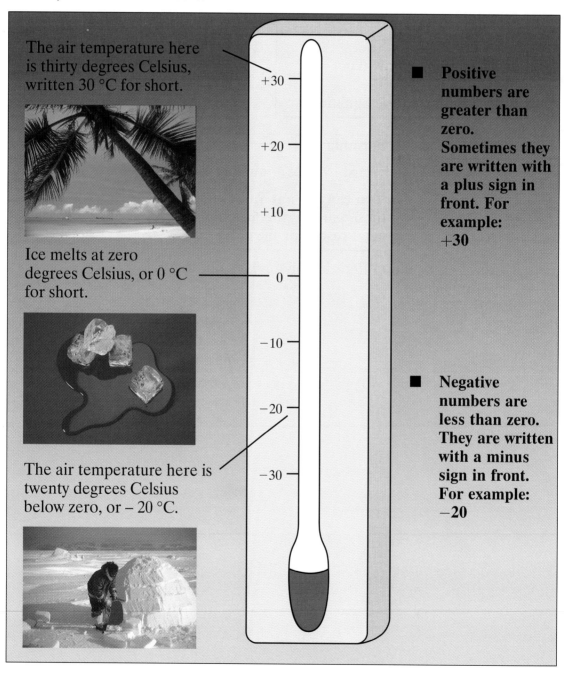

The air temperature here
is thirty degrees Celsius,
written 30 °C for short.

Ice melts at zero
degrees Celsius, or 0 °C
for short.

The air temperature here is
twenty degrees Celsius
below zero, or – 20 °C.

+30

+20

+10

0

−10

−20

−30

■ **Positive
numbers are
greater than
zero.
Sometimes they
are written with
a plus sign in
front. For
example:
+30**

■ **Negative
numbers are
less than zero.
They are written
with a minus
sign in front.
For example:
−20**

Example 1

What temperature does this thermometer show?
Write your answer
(a) in words
(b) in figures.

The temperature shown is six degrees below zero.
(a) in words: minus six degrees Celsius
(b) in figures: $-6\,°C$

Exercise 11A

In questions **1** to **12** look at the thermometer.
Write down the temperature it shows
(a) in words
(b) in figures.

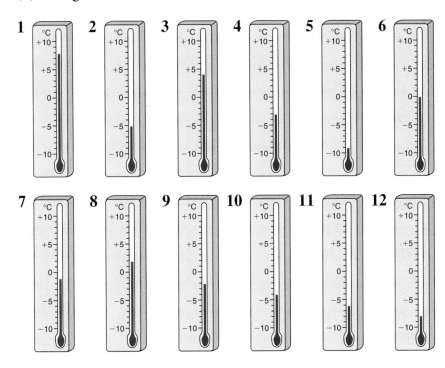

13   You need Activity sheet 8. On it show these
temperatures. The first one has been done for you.

(a) $+5\,°C$ **(b)** $-2\,°C$ **(c)** $0\,°C$ **(d)** $+8\,°C$

(e) $-4\,°C$ **(f)** $-3\,°C$ **(g)** $+6\,°C$ **(h)** $-6\,°C$

(i) $-1\,°C$ **(j)** $-8\,°C$ **(k)** $+4\,°C$ **(l)** $-7\,°C$

The symbol ° is
short for
degrees.

11.2 Finding highest and lowest values

This weather map shows temperatures around Europe in degrees Celsius:

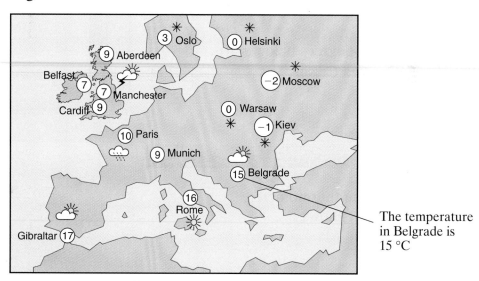

The temperature in Belgrade is 15 °C

Example 2

Use the weather map to find:

(a) the temperature in Paris in °C
(b) the temperature in Kiev in °C
(c) the highest temperature in °C
(d) the lowest temperature in °C

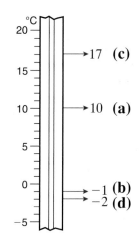

(a) The temperature in Paris is 10 °C
(b) The temperature in Kiev is −1 °C
(c) The highest temperature is 17 °C
(d) The lowest temperature is −2 °C

Example 3

Write down the highest and lowest temperatures from this list:

$$+3\,°C \quad +8\,°C \quad -2\,°C \quad 0\,°C \quad -5\,°C$$

To find the highest temperature look for the largest positive value. Here it is +8 °C.

To find the lowest temperature look for the largest negative value.

This is the largest number with a minus sign in front.
Here it is −5 °C.

Notice that −5 is less than −2

■ **In a list of positive and negative temperatures:**
To find the highest temperature look for the largest positive value.
To find the lowest temperature look for the largest negative value.

Exercise 11B

The weather maps in this Exercise show temperatures in degrees Celsius (°C)

1 Look at this weather map and write down the temperature in:

(a) London (b) Edinburgh
(c) Manchester (d) Belfast
(e) Cardiff (f) Birmingham
(g) Aberdeen (h) Exeter
(i) Newcastle

2 Use this weather map to find:

(a) the temperature in Norwich
(b) the temperature in Oxford
(c) the hottest place
(d) the coldest place

3 Look at this weather map and write down:

(a) the highest temperature
(b) the lowest temperature

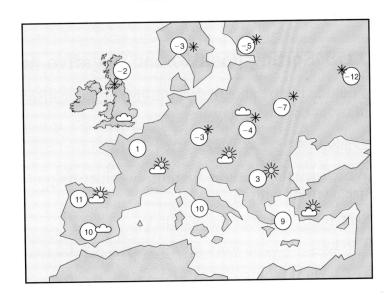

4 On this weather map what is:

(a) the highest temperature?

(b) the lowest temperature?

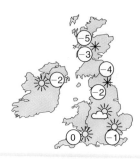

5 Write down the higher of the two temperatures:

(a) 2 °C and 5 °C   (b) 8 °C and 4 °C

(c) 3 °C and 0 °C   (d) −1 °C and 5 °C

(e) 4 °C and −2 °C   (f) −3 °C and −6 °C

6 Write down the lower of the two temperatures:

(a) 4 °C and 1 °C   (b) 0 °C and 2 °C

(c) −5 °C and 2 °C   (d) 0 °C and −4 °C

(e) 1 °C and −1 °C   (f) −5 °C and −10 °C

7 Write down the highest temperature in each list:

(a) +3 °C, −2 °C, +4 °C, −6 °C, +10 °C, −5 °C.

(b) +2 °C, +4 °C, −3 °C, −7 °C, 0 °C, +5 °C.

(c) −2 °C, −5 °C, 0 °C, −6 °C, −8 °C, −3 °C.

(d) −2 °C, −5 °C, −6 °C, −4 °C, −7 °C, −1 °C.

8 Write down the lowest temperature in each list:

(a) +3 °C, −2 °C, +4 °C, −6 °C, +10 °C, −5 °C.

(b) +2 °C, +4 °C, −3 °C, −7 °C, 0 °C, +5 °C.

(c) +8 °C, −7 °C, +3 °C, −4 °C, +5 °C, −3 °C.

(d) −2 °C, −1 °C, −8 °C, −7 °C, 0 °C, −6 °C.

11.3 Sorting positive and negative numbers

You need to be able to sort positive and negative numbers in order of size.

Example 4

Write the temperatures from this weather map in order of size, starting with the lowest.

Sketching a number line can help.

The lowest temperature on the map is −4 °C.

The highest temperature is +3 °C.

Draw a number line
from −4 to +3

Circle each temperature from
the weather map on your
number line:

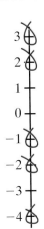

Write down the temperatures in order, starting from the
bottom:

−4 °C   −2 °C   −1 °C   2 °C   3 °C

■ **You can use a number line to help you sort numbers in
order of size.**

Exercise 11C

These weather maps show temperatures in degrees
Celsius (°C).

1 For each map write down the temperatures in order
of size.
Start with the lowest temperature each time.

(a)

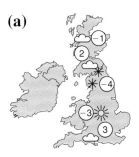

(b)

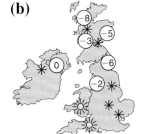

(c)

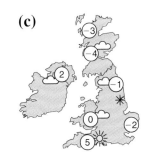

2 Write down the temperatures from this map in order of size. Start with the highest temperature.

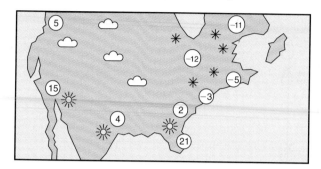

3 Write down these temperatures in order of size, starting with the highest.
(a) −3 °C, 0 °C, 4 °C, −2 °C, −6 °C, 10 °C.
(b) 4 °C, −3 °C, 2 °C, −7 °C, −6 °C, 1 °C.
(c) −3 °C, 2 °C, −1 °C, −8 °C, −5 °C, 0 °C.
(d) −7 °C, −3 °C, −4 °C, 0 °C, −1 °C, −10 °C.

4 Write down these temperatures in order of size, starting with the lowest.
(a) 5 °C, 0 °C, −4 °C, −8 °C, 1 °C, −3 °C.
(b) −4 °C, −9 °C, 2 °C, −1 °C, 8 °C, 5 °C.
(c) 1 °C, −4 °C, 3 °C, −5 °C, 6 °C, −10 °C.
(d) −2 °C, 3 °C, −8 °C, −5 °C, −1 °C, 6 °C.

11.4 From positive to negative and back again

This section uses the idea of a lift to help you use positive and negative numbers.

Taking the lift

In these flats numbers are used to name each floor.

Below ground level negative numbers are used.

fourth floor	4
third floor	3
second floor	2
first floor	1
ground floor	0
car park	−1
boiler room	−2

Example 5

Jenny gets in the lift at
floor −2 and goes up
3 floors.

Which floor is she at now?

Start at floor −2 and go
up 3 floors. Jenny is now
at floor 1.

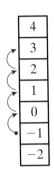

Example 6

Raffi gets in the lift at
floor −1 and goes down
1 floor.

Which floor is he at now?

Start at floor −1 and go
down 1 floor. Raffi is now
at floor −2.

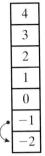

Example 7

Edward takes the lift
from floor −1 to floor 3.
How many floors has he
gone up?

From floor −1 to floor 3.

Edward has gone up
4 floors.

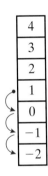

Example 8

Morag takes the lift
from floor 1 to floor −2.
How many floors has she
gone down?

From floor 1 to floor −2.

Morag has gone down
3 floors.

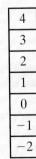

Exercise 11D

1 Write down the floor the lift gets to if:

  (a) it starts at floor 0 and goes up 2 floors.
  (b) it starts at floor 3 and goes down 2 floors.
  (c) it starts at floor −2 and goes up 4 floors.
  (d) it starts at floor 1 and goes down 3 floors.
  (e) it starts at floor −1 and goes down 1 floor.
  (f) it starts at floor 4 and goes down 6 floors.
  (g) it starts at floor 2 and goes down 3 floors.
  (h) it starts at floor −1 and goes up 3 floors.

Use a sketch like this
to help you answer
these questions.

```
 4
 3
 2
 1
 0
−1
−2
```

2 How many floors does the lift go up if it goes from:

  (a) floor 0 to floor 4   **(b)** floor −2 to floor 2
  (c) floor −1 to floor 3   **(d)** floor −2 to floor −1
  (e) floor −1 to floor 4   **(f)** floor −2 to floor 4.

3 How many floors does the lift go down if it goes from:
   (a) floor 2 to floor 0   **(b)** floor 1 to floor −2
   (c) floor 3 to floor −1   **(d)** floor 4 to floor −2
   (e) floor −1 to floor −2   **(f)** floor 2 to floor −2.

11.5 Temperatures rising and falling

You need to be able to measure temperature **changes**.

Example 9

The temperature in York at midnight was −4 °C.
By noon next day it had risen to 3 °C.
How much did the temperature rise?

A thermometer scale is like a number line:

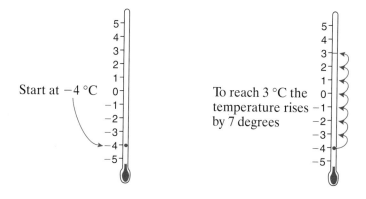

The temperature rose by 7 °C.

Exercise 11E

1 The temperature in Manchester at midnight was −3 °C.
By noon the next day the temperature had gone up to
2 °C. Work out the rise in the temperature.

2 The temperature in Cardiff at noon was 3 °C. By 8 pm
the same day the temperature had gone down to −1 °C.
Work out the fall in temperature.

3 The temperature in Norwich at midnight was −5 °C. By noon the next day the temperature had gone up by 8 °C. Work out the temperature in Norwich at noon.

4 The temperature in Sunderland at noon was −2 °C. By midnight the temperature had fallen by 6 °C. What was the temperature in Sunderland at midnight?

Use a number line like this to help you answer these questions

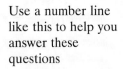
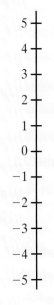

Copy and complete the tables for questions **5** and **6**.

5

Town	Temperature at midnight	Temperature at noon the next day	Temperature rise
Rotherham	−4 °C	4 °C	
Evesham	−2 °C	6 °C	
Skegness	−6 °C	−2 °C	
Reigate	−3 °C		8 °C
Blackpool	−5 °C		6 °C
Scarborough	−1 °C		5 °C

6

Town	Temperature at noon	Temperature at 2 am the next day	Temperature fall
Windsor	6 °C	2 °C	
Winchester	5 °C	−2 °C	
Kendal	−2 °C	−9 °C	
Scunthorpe	−1 °C		8 °C
Chester	2 °C		4 °C
Ipswich	−3 °C		7 °C

11.6 Using a number line

A number line can help you solve problems involving positive and negative numbers.

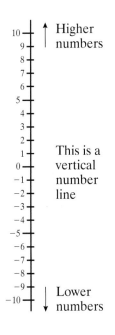

Example 10

(a) Start at −2 and go up 5. What number do you stop at?

(b) Start at 4 and go down to −5. How many have you gone down?

(a) You stop at number 3.

(b) You have gone down 9.

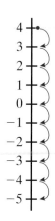

Example 11

Write down all the whole numbers between −4 and 3.

The lower of these two numbers is −4. Using a vertical number line write down all the numbers that are above −4 and below 3.

The numbers are −3, −2, −1, 0, 1, 2.

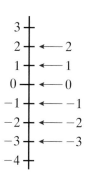

Example 12

Hannah chose an odd number that is bigger than −5 but smaller than −1.
What number did Hannah choose?

Using a vertical number line the numbers that are bigger than −5 and smaller than −1 are −4, −3 and −2. The only one of these that is an odd number is −3.

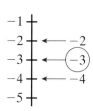

So Hannah chose the number −3.

Example 13

Write down the next two numbers in this pattern:

    11, 7, 3, −1,…

To get from one number to the next number in the pattern you take away 4. Using a vertical number line the next two numbers in the pattern are −5 and −9.

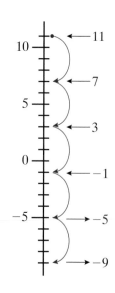

Exercise 11F

Use a vertical number line to help you with these questions.

1 Emma chooses two cards at a time from a set of numbered cards. These are the numbers on them each time. Which is the higher number each time?
(a) −2, +4 (b) +2, −3 (c) +3, −6 (d) −7, +4
(e) +1, +6 (f) −5, +2 (g) −7, −4 (h) −3, −9

2 Which is the lowest number:
(a) −2 or +6   (b) −3 or +1   (c) −2 or +7
(d) +8 or −4   (e) +7 or +2   (f) −7 or +4
(g) −3 or −6   (h) −8 or −5   (i) −2 or −4

3 Write down all the whole numbers between:
(a) −3 and 2   (b) −5 and 1   (c) −7 and −2
(d) −4 and 5   (e) −6 and 3   (f) −8 and −3
(g) −2 and −5   (h) −4 and −6   (i) −1 and 4

4 Write down the result of these:
(a) Start at −5 and go up 3
(b) Start at −2 and go up 4
(c) Start at −3 and go up 7
(d) Start at 2 and go up 5
(e) Start at −4 and go up 4
(f) Start at −7 and go up 10

5 Shannon chose an even number that is larger than −6 but smaller than −3. What number did Shannon choose?

6 Luke chooses a number that is smaller than −4, larger than −7 and is odd. What number did Luke choose?

7 Write down the next two numbers in each pattern:
(a) 7, 4, 1, −2, . . .   (b) 9, 5, 1, −3, . . .
(c) 7, 5, 3, 1, . . .   (d) 8, 6, 4, 2, . . .
(e) 2, −1, −4, −7, . . .   (f) −1, −3, −5, −7, . . .
(g) −13, −10, −7, −4, . . .   (h) −11, −7, −3, 1, . . .
(i) 6, 5, 3, 0, . . .   (j) −7, −6, −4, −1, . . .

10
9
8
7
6
5
4
3
2
1
0
−1
−2
−3
−4
−5
−6
−7
−8
−9
−10

8 **Activity**   A game for two players.
You need a dice and two counters.

Copy the vertical strip opposite.

Place the counters on 0.

Take turns to throw the dice.

- If the number is **even**, move **up** the strip.
  Move up the number shown on the dice.

- If the number is **odd**, move **down** the strip.
  Move down the number shown on the dice.

The first player to reach +10 or −10 wins.

9 **Investigation**   Play the game in question **8**.

(a) Keep a list of the numbers you throw on the dice each time you play.

(b) Investigate the numbers you need to land on the −1 square.

(c) Can you land on all the negative number squares?

Summary of key points

1 Positive numbers are greater than zero. Sometimes they are written with a plus sign + in front.
For example: +30

2 Negative numbers are less than zero. They are written with a minus sign in front.
For example: −30

3 In a list of positive and negative temperatures:
To find the highest temperature look for the largest positive value.
To find the lowest temperature look for the largest negative value.

4 You can use a number line to help you sort numbers in order of size.

12 Graphs

12.1 Reading coordinates

This grid shows the positions of places on an island.
You can use two numbers to describe where a place is.

For example: the school is 3 units across and 4 units up,
written (3, 4). The numbers (3, 4) are the **coordinates**.

You always start
at 0

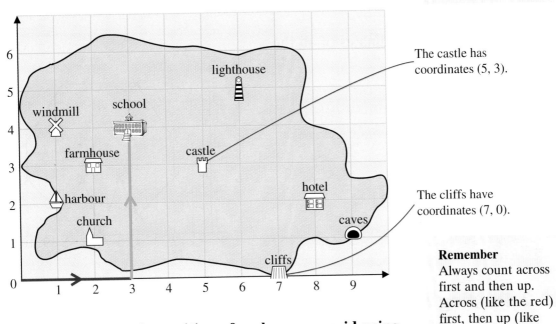

The castle has
coordinates (5, 3).

The cliffs have
coordinates (7, 0).

Remember
Always count across
first and then up.
Across (like the red)
first, then up (like
the blue).

■ **You can give the position of a place on a grid using coordinates.**

Exercise 12A

Look at the map of the island.

1   What is at each of these coordinates?
   (a) (2, 1) **(b)** (1, 4) **(c)** (6, 5) **(d)** (1, 2) **(e)** (7, 0)

2   What are the coordinates of these places on the island?
   (a) lighthouse **(b)** hotel **(c)** church
   (d) farmhouse **(e)** caves **(f)** harbour

3 Look at this map of a zoo:
What is at each of these coordinates?
(a) (4, 0) **(b)** (3, 3) **(c)** (0, 3)
(d) (6, 5) **(e)** (2, 6)

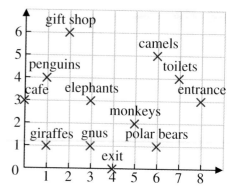

4 What are the coordinates of each of these places?
(a) camels **(b)** toilets **(c)** entrance
(d) giraffes **(e)** gnus

5 Write down the coordinates of all the
corners in this shape:

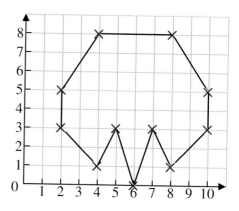

12.2 Plotting coordinates

You can draw your own grid on squared paper and plot coordinates on it.

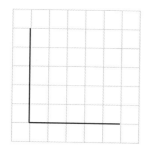

Draw two lines on squared
paper, one horizontal and
one vertical. These lines
are called **axes**.

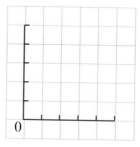

Mark each axis like this.
Where the axes cross,
write 0.

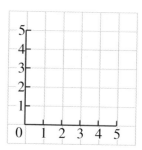

Number each axis.
Write the numbers in order.

Example 1

Draw a coordinate grid.
Number each axis from 0 to 10.

Plot these points on your grid:
(1, 1)   (2, 9)   (7, 3).

Join each point in order.
Join the last point to the first.
What shape do you get?

The shape is a triangle.

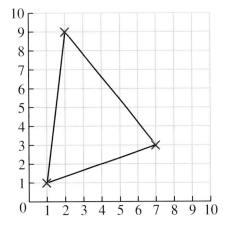

Exercise 12B

You need squared paper for this exercise.

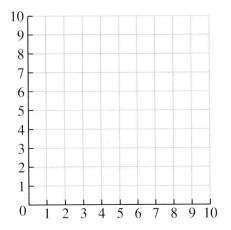

1   Draw a coordinate grid.
Number each axis from 0 to 10.

Draw a treasure island with these places:

cliffs, palm trees, lookout tower,
buried treasure, oasis, harbour, graveyard,
pirate camp, navy camp, cave.

Write down the coordinates of each place.

2   Draw a coordinate grid. Number each axis
from 0 to 10.
 ● Plot these points on your grid:
    (0, 2) (2, 1) (8, 1) (10, 2) (5, 2) (5, 8)
    (5, 7) (2, 3) (8, 3) (5, 8) (5, 2) (0, 2)
 ● Join each point to the last point you plotted.
 ● Join the last point to the first to make a shape.
 ● Shade the shape.
    You should get a ship.

3   Draw three coordinate grids.
Number each axis from 0 to 10.
For each set of points below:
 ● Plot the points.
 ● Join them up to make a shape.
 (a) (6, 10)   (9, 10)   (9, 7)   (6, 7)
 (b) (7, 1)   (10, 6)   (10, 1)
 (c) (4, 4)   (5, 6)   (8, 6)   (7, 4)
Try to name each shape.

4 Draw a coordinate grid.
Number the across axis from 0 to 10.
Number the up axis from 0 to 6.
Plot these points:

   (1, 4) (2, 6) (3, 4) (5, 4) (6, 6)
   (7, 4) (7, 2) (4, 0) (1, 2) (1, 4)

Join the points to make a shape.

5 Draw three coordinate grids.
Number each axis from 0 to 10.
Plot each set of points on a grid:
   (a) Square: (1, 1)   (5, 1)   (1, 5)
   (b) Rectangle: (2, 7)   (7, 7)   (7, 10)
   (c) Rectangle: (8, 4)   (8, 9)   (10, 9)

Each shape has a corner missing.
Write down the coordinates of each missing corner.

6 Draw a coordinate grid.
Number each axis from 0 to 10.
Draw a shape of your own.
Write down the coordinates of each point.

Example 2

Two teams take turns to put a counter on
the grid.

To win the game, get four of your counters in
a straight line.
The line can be across, up or slanted.

This game has been started. It is blue's turn.
Can blue win the game with the next counter?
Write down the coordinates of the points
that make a winning line.

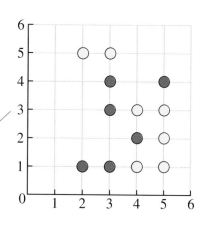

Yes. If they put a counter at (3, 2) they can
win the game.
(3, 1), (3, 2), (3, 3) and (3, 4) make a
vertical line.

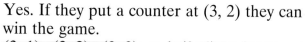

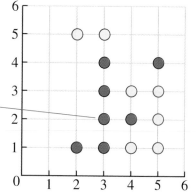

Exercise 12C

1   Look at the grid in Example 2 opposite. Where could the yellow team go to win the game? Write down the coordinates of the points that make a winning line.

2   Draw a grid. Number each axis from 0 to 6. Plot these moves on your grid:
    Yellow: (4, 3) (3, 2) (5, 3) (4, 2) (6, 4) (2, 2)
    Blue: (6, 1) (5, 4) (6, 3) (6, 2) (3, 1) (5, 1)
    If it is yellow's turn next, where should they go?
    If it is blue's turn next, where should they go?
    Write down the coordinates of the points that make a winning line.

3   Play your own game.
    Keep a record of all the coordinates each team uses.
    Which team wins the game?
    Write down the coordinates of the points that make a winning line.

12.3 Using graphs to show relationships

Martin is selling tickets for a school disco.
Each ticket costs £2.

The total cost depends on how many tickets you buy. The cost and the number of tickets you buy are related.

Martin uses this graph to work out the cost quickly.

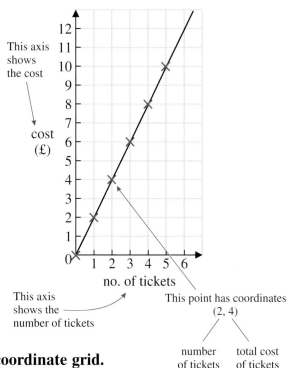

This axis shows the cost

cost (£)

no. of tickets

This axis shows the number of tickets

This point has coordinates (2, 4)

number of tickets   total cost of tickets

So 2 tickets cost £4.

■ **Graphs show a relationship on a coordinate grid. For example, how many tickets you buy and the total cost of the tickets.**

How to use the graph

How much do 6 tickets cost?

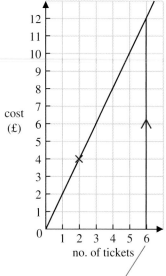

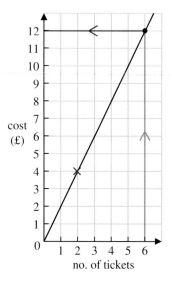

Find 6 tickets on this axis. Draw
a vertical line up to the graph.

Draw a horizontal line from the
graph to the cost axis. Read off
the price. 6 tickets cost £12.

How many tickets can you buy for £8?

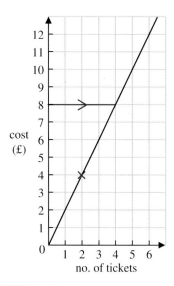

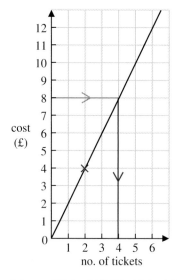

Find £8 on the cost axis.
Draw a horizontal line across
to the graph.

Draw a vertical line from the graph
to the ticket axis. Read off the number
of tickets. £8 will buy 4 tickets.

Exercise 12D

1   Football stickers cost 25p each.
The cost of a number of
stickers is shown on
the graph.

Use the graph to answer these
questions:

(a) How much will 9 stickers
cost?

(b) How many stickers can I
buy with £1.50?

Hint: £1.50 is 150p

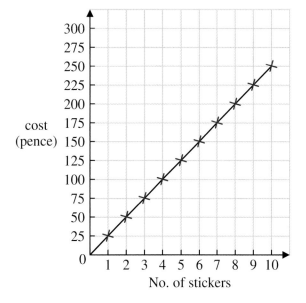

2   Concert tickets cost £5 each.
Use the graph to answer the
questions.

(a) How much will 7 tickets cost?

(b) How much will 4 tickets cost?

(c) How many tickets can you
buy with £45?

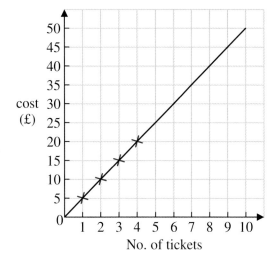

3   This graph is used to work out the
cost of bags of crisps in the school
tuckshop.

(a) How much is 1 bag of crisps?

(b) How many bags can you buy
with 60p?

(c) How much do 7 bags of crisps
cost?

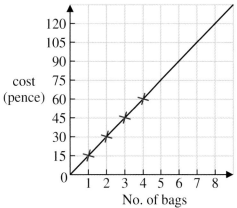

4 This graph shows the cost of potatoes.

Use the graph to find the cost of:

(a) 6 kg of potatoes
(b) 9 kg of potatoes.

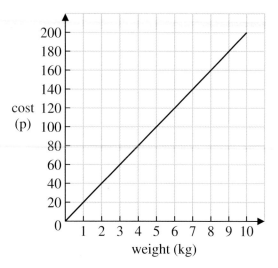

5 This graph is used to work out the cost of milk shakes in the tuckshop.

(a) How much do 5 milk shakes cost?

Hint: 75 is halfway between 70 and 80.

(b) How much does 1 milk shake cost?

(c) How many milk shakes can you buy with £1.05? (£1.05 is 105p)

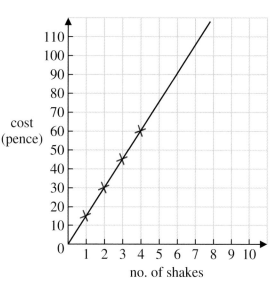

6 The graph shows the amount of petrol left in the tank of a van during a journey.

(a) After how many hours will the van run out of petrol?

(b) How many litres of petrol did the tank hold at the start of the journey?

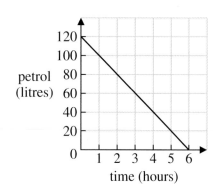

7 Mary charges £2 for the use of her taxi and £1 for each mile of the journey. The graph shows the charge for different journeys.

(a) What will a journey of 10 miles cost?
(b) What will a journey of 7 miles cost?
(c) How far can you travel for £10?
(d) How far can you travel for £7?

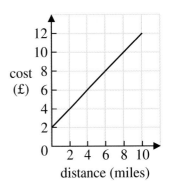

Exercise 12E

1 Sanjay is lost in a maze.
He knows he is at the point (2, 6).

Ravi is shouting instructions to Sanjay to help him get out of the maze: 'Move to (1, 6). Now move to (1, 5). Now to (1, 4).'

The moves are shown on the grid.

Write down the list of moves Ravi should shout to get Sanjay out of the maze.

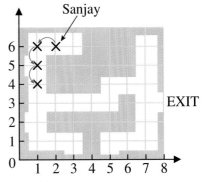

2 Write down a list of moves to help Gary get out of this maze.

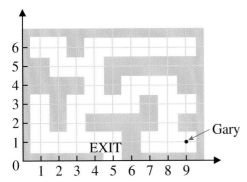

3 The grid shows a game of battleships.

What coordinates should you give to sink:

(a) the aircraft carrier
(b) the battleship
(c) the other two submarines?

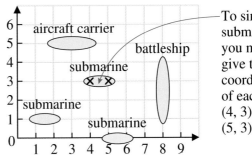

To sink this submarine you must give the coordinates of each point: (4, 3) and (5, 3).

4 Design your own game of battleships and play it with a friend.

Summary of key points

1 You can give the position of a place on a grid using coordinates. For example: the school is 3 units across and 4 units up, written (3, 4). The numbers (3, 4) are the **coordinates**.

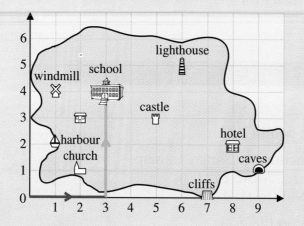

Remember:
You always start at 0.
Always count across first and then up.
Across (like the red) first, then up (like the blue).

2 Graphs show a relationship on a coordinate grid. For example, how many tickets you buy and the total cost of the tickets.

3 You can read a graph like this:

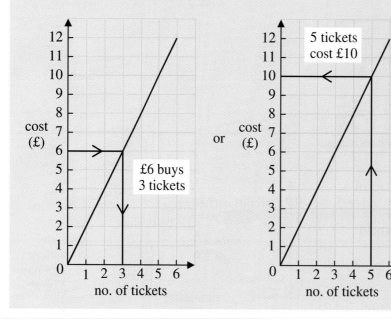

13 Angles

Kate is a gymnast.

She starts like this:	She has made a quarter turn	She has made a half turn	She has made a three quarter turn	She is back at the start

$\frac{1}{4}$ turn $\qquad$ $\frac{1}{2}$ turn $\qquad$ $\frac{3}{4}$ turn $\qquad$ full turn

This unit shows you how to measure turns.

13.1 Turning

You can measure a turn using simple fractions like $\frac{1}{4}$, $\frac{1}{2}$, $\frac{3}{4}$

Remember:
A fraction of a turn is part of a full turn.
There is more about fractions on page 121

■ **Turns can be:**
clockwise $\qquad$ **or anticlockwise**

Clock hands turn this way

Example 1

Describe these turns:

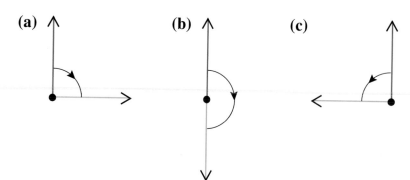

(a) $\frac{1}{4}$ turn clockwise   **(b)** $\frac{1}{2}$ turn clockwise   **(c)** $\frac{1}{4}$ turn anticlockwise

Exercise 13A

Which letter will the arrow point to when it makes:

1 $\frac{1}{4}$ turn clockwise from A

2 $\frac{1}{4}$ turn anticlockwise from B

3 $\frac{1}{2}$ turn from F

4 $\frac{1}{4}$ turn clockwise from E

5 $\frac{1}{2}$ turn from H

6 $\frac{1}{4}$ turn anticlockwise from C

7 $\frac{1}{4}$ turn anticlockwise from G

8 $\frac{1}{4}$ turn clockwise from F

9 $\frac{1}{2}$ turn from D

10 $\frac{1}{4}$ turn clockwise from H

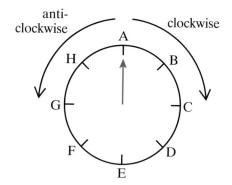

Describe the turn needed to move from:

11 C to E	12 F to D	13 B to F
14 E to C	15 D to F	16 A to C
17 D to B	18 H to D	19 B to D

13.2 Turning it

You can trace a shape: and turn it:

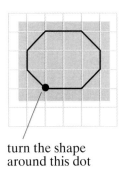

turn the shape
around this dot

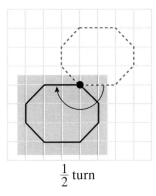

$\frac{1}{4}$ turn $\frac{1}{2}$ turn

Exercise 13B

Trace each shape.
Draw each shape when it has turned around the dot:

(a) $\frac{1}{4}$ turn clockwise   **(b)** $\frac{1}{2}$ turn   **(c)** $\frac{3}{4}$ turn clockwise

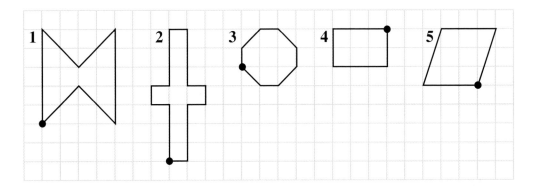

13.3 Rotations

■ **A rotation is a turn.**

Whose turn
is it next?

Example 2

Rotate this shape clockwise around the dot:

(a) $\frac{1}{4}$ turn   **(b)** $\frac{1}{2}$ turn   **(c)** $\frac{3}{4}$ turn

(d) When does it look exactly the same as the original shape?

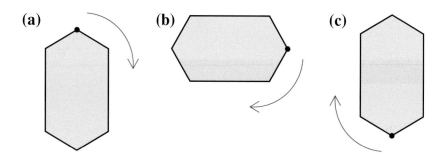

(d) It looks the same after $\frac{1}{2}$ turn.

Exercise 13C

Rotate each shape around the dot:

(a) $\frac{1}{4}$ turn   **(b)** $\frac{1}{2}$ turn   **(c)** $\frac{3}{4}$ turn

(d) When does it look exactly the same as the original shape?

Hint: instead of tracing the shape you could turn the page round.

1   2   3   4   5

6   7   8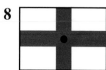

13.4 Rotational symmetry

This flag looks exactly the same as the original after a rotation of $\frac{1}{2}$ turn:

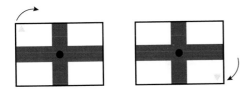

■ **A shape has rotational symmetry if it looks exactly the same after a rotation.**

A full turn doesn't count!

Exercise 13D

1   Which shapes in Exercise **13C** have rotational symmetry?

2   Trace each of these shapes. Put a cross through each shape which does not have rotational symmetry

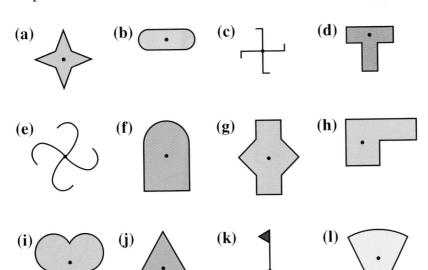

13.5 Measuring turns

These turns are difficult to measure using simple fractions:

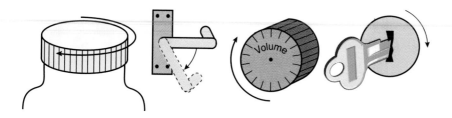

Instead of fractions you can use **angles** to describe the rotation.

■ **An angle is a measure of turn.**
  An angle is usually measured in degrees,
  ° for short.

■ **There are 360° in a full turn.**

Why 360° for a full turn?
4 thousand years ago, people thought there were 360 days in a year. That's 360 days for the Earth to go round the Sun.

Here are some turns measured in degrees:

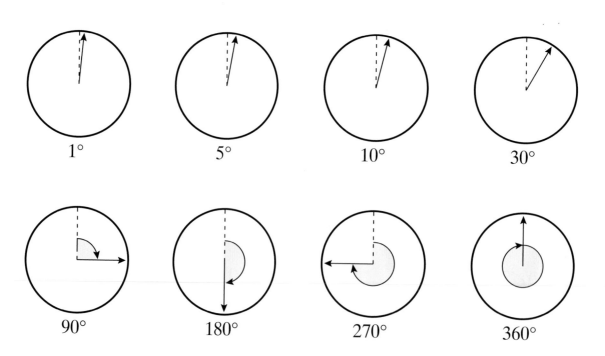

1°   5°   10°   30°

90°   180°   270°   360°

Exercise 13E

1   How many degrees are there in these turns?
     Choose from these answers:

0°, 10°, 30°, 45°, 60°, 80°, 90°, 120°, 180°,
270°, 350°, 360°.

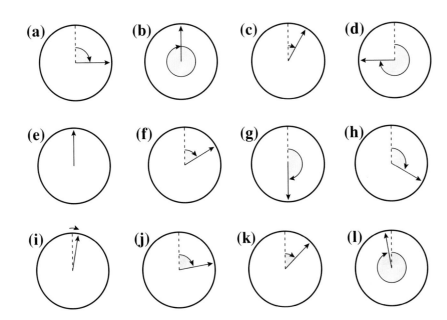

(a) (b) (c) (d)

(e) (f) (g) (h)

(i) (j) (k) (l)

13.6 Using a protractor

A protractor measures angles in degrees.

It looks like this:

You can use an angle
measurer instead of a
protractor.

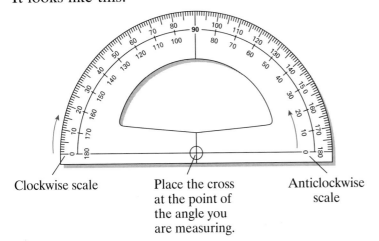

Clockwise scale   Place the cross
                   at the point of
                   the angle you
                   are measuring.

Anticlockwise
scale

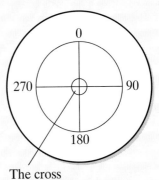

The cross
is at the centre.

Example 3

Measure the angle between these lines using a protractor:

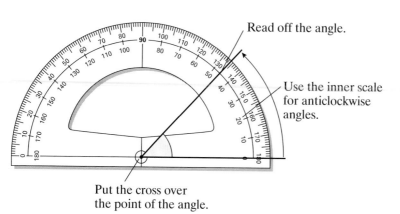

Read off the angle.

Use the inner scale for anticlockwise angles.

Put the cross over the point of the angle.

The angle is 46°.

■ **The angle between two lines is the amount of turn from one line to the other.**

Use a protractor to measure these angles.

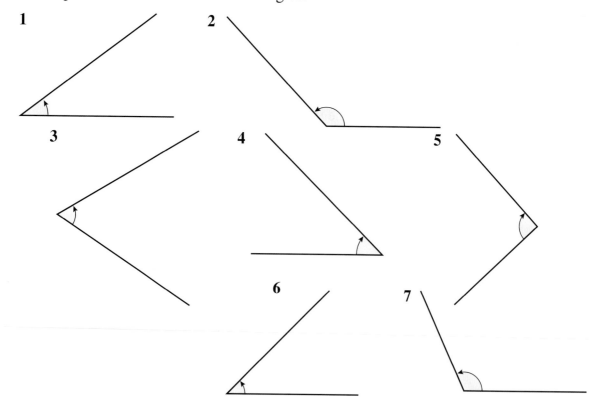

1

2

3

4

5

6

7

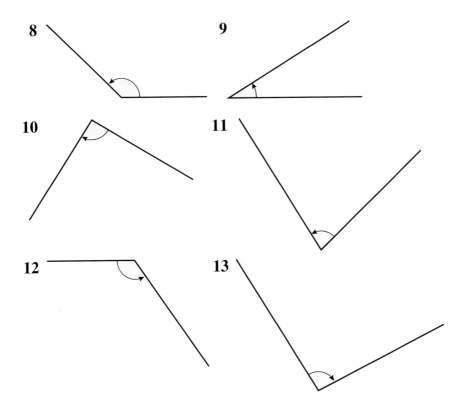

13.7 Angle types

The angle between these lines is 90°.   The angle between these lines is 180°.

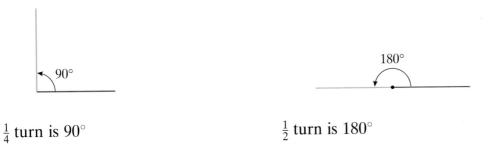

$\frac{1}{4}$ turn is 90° $\frac{1}{2}$ turn is 180°

You name an angle depending on its size.

■ $\frac{1}{4}$ **turn or 90°**   **smaller than 90°**   **larger than 90°**

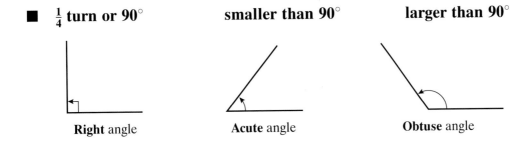

Right angle   **Acute** angle   **Obtuse** angle

Example 4

(a) Which angles are acute?
(b) Which angles are obtuse?

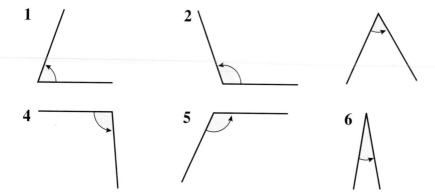

Compare the angles to the corner of your book.

(a) 1, 3 and 6 and acute angles.
(b) 2, 4 and 5 are obtuse angles.

Exercise 13G

For each angle, write down if it is an acute angle, right angle or obtuse angle.

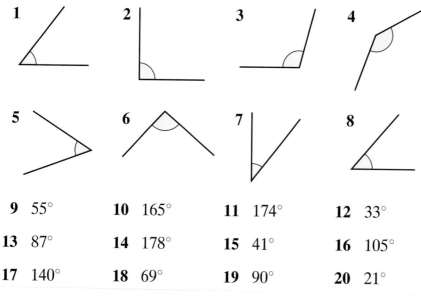

9 55°	**10** 165°	**11** 174°	**12** 33°
13 87°	**14** 178°	**15** 41°	**16** 105°
17 140°	**18** 69°	**19** 90°	**20** 21°

21 How many degrees are there in

(a) $\frac{1}{2}$ turn? (b) $\frac{1}{4}$ turn? (c) a full turn? (d) $\frac{3}{4}$ turn?

13.8 Drawing angles

You can draw an angle using a protractor.

Example 5

Draw these angles:

(a) 30°   **(b)** 110°

(a)

Draw a straight line.   Put the protractor on the line like this: Make a mark at 30°. Use anticlockwise scale.   Join the mark to the end of the line.

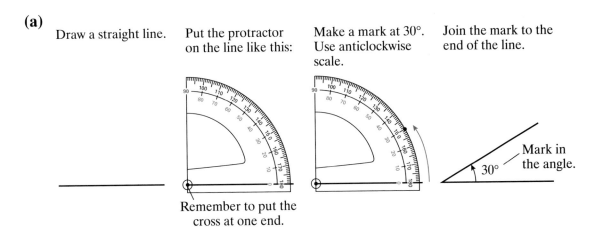

Remember to put the cross at one end.

Mark in the angle.

(b) Make a mark at 110°.   Join the mark to the line:

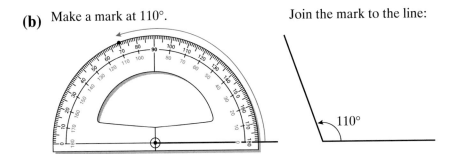

Exercise 13H

Draw these angles:

1 80°	**2** 55°	**3** 30°	**4** 125°
5 65°	**6** 25°	**7** 145°	**8** 45°
9 160°	**10** 35°	**11** 150°	**12** 75°
13 70°	**14** 23°	**15** 16°	**16** 136°

13.9 Estimating angles

You should be able to estimate the size of an angle.

You can compare it to a right angle.

Example 6

Estimate these angles:

(a)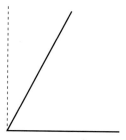

(b)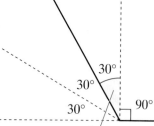

(a) This is an acute angle.
Compare it to a right angle:

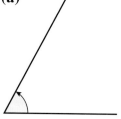

It is just over $\frac{1}{2}$ way.
A good estimate is 50°.

(b) This is an obtuse angle.
Look at the part that is over 90°.

This is about $\frac{1}{3}$ of a right angle.
Remember: to find $\frac{1}{3}$ you divide by 3
$90 \div 3 = 30°$
So the angle is about $90° + 30° = 120°$

Exercise 13I

Estimate the sizes of these angles:

1

2

3

4

5

6

7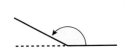

8

9

10

11

12

13

14

15

16

17

18

Summary of key points

1   Turns can be:

clockwise   or anticlockwise

Clock hands turn
this way

2   A rotation is a turn.

3   A shape has rotational symmetry if it looks exactly the same after a rotation.
A full turn doesn't count!

4   An angle is a measure of turn.
An angle is usually measured in degrees, ° for short.

5   There are 360° in a full turn.

6   The angle between two lines is the amount of turn from one line to the other.

7 $\frac{1}{4}$ turn or 90°   smaller than 90°   larger than 90°

Right angle

Acute angle

Obtuse angle

14 Handling data

You often see information given in tables and charts.

This unit shows you how to collect information and show it in tables and charts like these:

How 12 year olds spend their leisure time

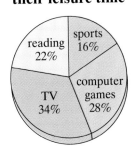

Number of visitors to Green's swimming pool last year

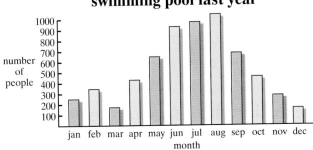

- Data is another word for information.

14.1 Collecting data from surveys

Bill runs a sweet shop. He wants to know which crisps will sell best.

To find out he does a survey.

He asks the next 30 customers:

'Which flavour of crisps do you like most?'

Here are some of the replies:

Bacon, Salt and vinegar, Cheese and onion, Salt and vinegar, Plain, Bacon, Prawn cocktail, Salt and vinegar, ...

This is part of Bill's data.

- You can collect data using a survey.

Exercise 14A

Carry out these surveys on the people in your class.
Write down a list of their answers.

1   People's favourite lesson.
    Ask: 'What is your favourite lesson'.

2   Days of the week people were born.
    Ask: 'What day of the week were you born?'

3   Number of children in people's family.

4   Number of pets people have.

5   Colour of people's eyes.

14.2 Collecting data from experiments

Josh wants to know if his dice is fair.

He rolls the dice 60 times.

He keeps a list of the scores:

1	6	3	5	1	3	3	2	4	6
4	4	2	6	1	1	5	3	5	5
4	6	3	1	2	2	2	2	4	5
1	1	6	5	6	6	4	5	3	5
3	4	4	5	5	6	1	6	2	6

■ **You can collect data from an experiment.**

If the dice is fair you would expect roughly the same number of each score.

Exercise 14B

Carry out these experiments.

1   Roll a dice 60 times.
    Write down a list of the scores shown on the dice.

2   Roll two dice 60 times.
    Add together the scores shown on the
    two dice.
    Keep a list of the total scores.

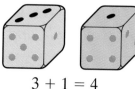

$3 + 1 = 4$

3   Toss a coin 50 times.
    Write down a list showing whether it lands on heads or
    tails.

14.3 Organizing data

If you organize data it makes it easier to spot any patterns.

You can use a table to organize data.

Example 1

Here is Bill's data on favourite flavours of crisps.

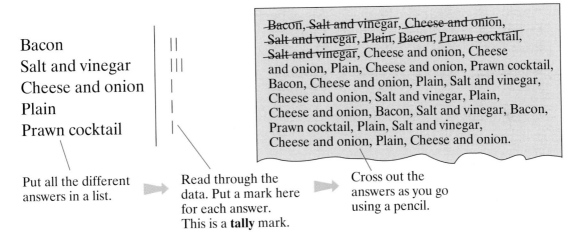

Bacon ||
Salt and vinegar |||
Cheese and onion |
Plain |
Prawn cocktail |

Bacon, Salt and vinegar, Cheese and onion, Salt and vinegar, Plain, Bacon, Prawn cocktail, Salt and vinegar, Cheese and onion, Cheese and onion, Plain, Cheese and onion, Prawn cocktail, Bacon, Cheese and onion, Plain, Salt and vinegar, Cheese and onion, Salt and vinegar, Plain, Cheese and onion, Bacon, Salt and vinegar, Bacon, Prawn cocktail, Plain, Salt and vinegar, Cheese and onion, Plain, Cheese and onion.

Put all the different answers in a list. ➡ Read through the data. Put a mark here for each answer. This is a **tally** mark. ➡ Cross out the answers as you go using a pencil.

The complete table is called a **tally chart**.

Flavour	Tally	Total
Bacon	⊬⊬⊬	5
Salt and vinegar	⊬⊬⊬ ||	7
Cheese and onion	⊬⊬⊬ ||||	9
Plain	⊬⊬⊬		6
Prawn cocktail	|||	3
		30

This tally ⊬⊬⊬ means 5

Bunch the tally marks in 5s. Then they are easier to count. ➡ Count up the tally marks. Put the total here. ➡ Count up all the totals to check you have used all the data 5 + 7 + 9 + 6 + 3 = 30.

■ **You can use a tally chart to organize data.**

Exercise 14C

1   Organize the data you collected for each question in
Exercise **14A**.
Follow the steps in Example 1 to make tally charts.

> Remember to check you have used all the data.

2   Make a tally chart for the data you collected in
Exercise **14B**.
Follow the steps in Example 1.

3   This is a list of people's favourite fruit:

Apple	Pear	Pear	Strawberry	Pear
Peach	Grape	Orange	Grape	Banana
Pear	Peach	Banana	Peach	Strawberry
Orange	Pear	Peach	Apple	Banana
Strawberry	Pear	Peach	Orange	Peach

Make a tally chart for this data.

14.4 Using tally charts

Bill uses his tally chart to decide which crisps to
stock in his shop.

The most popular flavour is Cheese and onion.
The least popular flavour is Prawn cocktail.

He stocks more of the most popular crisps.

Flavour	Total
Bacon	5
Salt and vinegar	7
Cheese and onion	9
Plain	6
Prawn cocktail	3

Exercise 14D

1   This tally chart shows the eye colours of people in
class 7C:

> Here frequency means how often each eye colour occurs.

Colour of eyes	Tally	Frequency
Brown	JHT III	8
Blue	JHT JHT II	12
Green	III	3
Grey	II	2

(a) Which eye colour was most frequent?

(b) Which eye colour was least frequent?

(c) How many people are in class 7C?

2 This tally chart shows people's favourite chocolate bar:

Chocolate bar	Tally	Frequency
Plain	JHT II	7
White	JHT I	6
Coffee	IIII	4
Orange	JHT IIII	9
Milk	JHT JHT II	12
Fruit and nut	III	3

(a) Which was the most popular bar?

(b) Which was the least popular?

(c) How many people took part in the survey?

3 This tally chart shows the number of pets the pupils in class 7B have:

Number of pets	Tally	Frequency
0	III	
1	JHT III	
2	JHT II	
3	IIII	
4	JHT	
5	II	

(a) Copy the tally chart.
Complete the frequency column.

(b) What was the most frequent number of pets?

(c) How many people took part in the survey?

14.5 Using pictures to show data

Often you need to show data to other
people.

■ **A pictogram uses pictures to
represent quantities.**

Bill uses a packet of crisps instead of a
tallymark:

Bacon	CRISPS CRISPS CRISPS CRISPS CRISPS
Salt and vinegar	CRISPS CRISPS CRISPS CRISPS CRISPS CRISPS CRISPS
Cheese and onion	CRISPS CRISPS CRISPS CRISPS CRISPS CRISPS CRISPS CRISPS CRISPS
Plain	CRISPS CRISPS CRISPS CRISPS CRISPS CRISPS
Prawn cocktail	CRISPS CRISPS CRISPS

In Bill's pictogram each crisp packet represents one reply
from his survey.

Example 2

Draw a pictogram to show this data:

Number on a dice	Tally	Frequency
1	卌	5
2	卌	6
3						4
4	卌 ||	7
5					3
6						4

Use a dice instead of a tally mark:

Number on dice

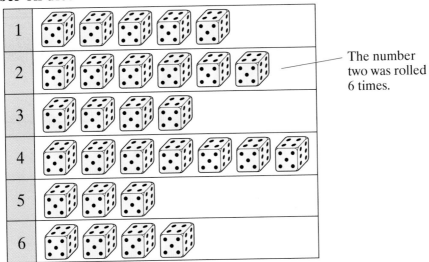

The number two was rolled 6 times.

Exercise 14E

1 Draw a pictogram for the data you collected in Exercise **14A**.

2 Draw a pictogram for the data you collected in Exercise **14B**.

3 This pictogram shows how pupils in 7B get to school:

Car	웃웃웃웃웃웃웃웃
Cycle	웃웃웃웃웃웃
Walk	웃웃웃웃웃웃웃웃웃
Bus	웃웃웃웃
Train	웃웃

Each 웃 represents one pupil.

(a) How many pupils come by car?
(b) How many pupils come by bus?
(c) What is the most frequent way of getting to school?
(d) How many pupils are there in the survey?

4 This pictogram shows how Naomi spends her weekly pocket money:

Travel	
Clothes	
Magazines	
Sweets	
Entertainment	
Saving	

Each represents £1.

(a) What does she spend most on?

(b) What does she spend least on?

(c) How much pocket money does she get each week?

14.6 Using a key

You can save time drawing a pictogram if you use each picture to stand for a number greater than one.

Example 3

Draw a pictogram to show this data.

Use to stand for 2 people.

Favourite drink	Tally	Frequency
Tea	JHT JHT II	12
Coffee	JHT JHT JHT	14
Coke	JHT JHT JHT III	18
Lemonade	JHT JHT	10
Orange	JHT III	8
Water	IIII	4

stands for 2 people so divide the frequencies by 2.

$12 \div 2 = 6$ $14 \div 2 = 7$ $18 \div 2 = 9$

$10 \div 2 = 5$ $8 \div 2 = 4$ $4 \div 2 = 2$

Draw the pictogram:

Tea	👤👤👤👤👤👤
Coffee	👤👤👤👤👤👤👤
Coke	👤👤👤👤👤👤👤👤👤
Lemonade	👤👤👤👤👤
Orange	👤👤👤👤
Water	👤👤

👤 stands for 2 people ——— This is called a **key**. It unlocks the meaning of your pictogram.

Example 4

This pictogram shows the drinks people like best:

Tea	🥤🥤
Coffee	🥤🥤🥤🥤🥤🥤
Coke	🥤🥤🥤🥤🥤🥤🥤
Orange	🥤🥤🥤
Milk	🥤🥤🥤
Lemonade	🥤🥤🥤🥤

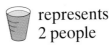 represents 2 people

(a) How many people like tea best?

(b) How many people like coffee best?

(c) How many people took part in the survey?

(a)

2 + 2 = 4 people

(b)

2 + 2 + 2 + 2 + 2 + 1 = 11 people

(c) Count all the full cups: 25 full cups

25 × 2 = 50 people.

Count all the half cups:

3 half cups = 3 people.

So 50 + 3 = 53 people took part altogether.

Exercise 14F

1 Draw a pictogram to show this data:

Favourite sport on TV	Tally	Frequency
Motor racing	JHT III	8
Football	JHT JHT JHT I	16
Rugby	JHT JHT II	12
Cricket	II	2
Golf	IIII	4
Darts	JHT JHT IIII	14

Use to stand for 2 people.

2 Draw a pictogram to show this data:

Favourite flavour of crisps	Tally	Frequency
Plain	JHT III	8
Cheese and onion	JHT JHT JHT JHT	20
Bacon	JHT JHT II	12
Salt and vinegar	JHT JHT JHT I	16
Prawn cocktail	IIII	4
Tomato sauce	II	2

Use to stand for 4 people.

3 This pictogram shows peoples favourite fruit.

Apple	🙂 🙂
Banana	🙂 🙂 🙂 🙂
Orange	🙂 🙂 🙂 🙂 🙂 🙂
Strawberry	🙂 🙂 🙂 🙂 🙂
Peach	🙂 🙂 🙂
Nectarine	🙂 🙂 🙂 🙂

🙂 stands for 2 people

(a) How many people liked strawberries best?

(b) How many people liked bananas best?

(c) How many people took part in the survey?

4 This pictogram shows the number of letters delivered to a school one week:

Monday	✉ ✉ ✉ ✉ ✉ ✉
Tuesday	✉ ✉ ✉
Wednesday	✉ ✉ ✉ ✉ ✉ ✉ ✉ ✉
Thursday	✉ ✉ ✉ ✉ ✉ ✉
Friday	✉ ✉ ✉ ✉
Saturday	✉ ✉ ✉

✉ stands for 10 letters

(a) How many letters were delivered on Tuesday?

(b) How many letters were delivered on Thursday?

(c) On which days were more than 50 letters delivered?

(d) How many letters were delivered in total?

14.7 Using bar charts to show data

■ **A bar chart uses bars or blocks to show data.**

Example 5

Draw a bar chart to show Bill's data from page 201.

Flavour	Total
Bacon	5
Salt and vinegar	7
Cheese and onion	9
Plain	6
Prawn cocktail	3

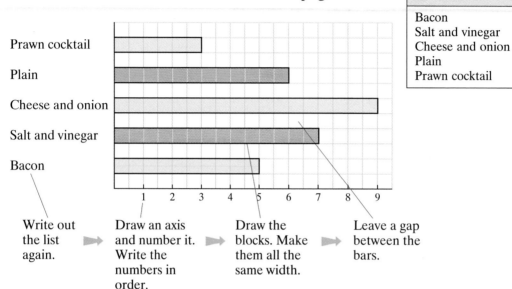

Write out the list again. ➡ Draw an axis and number it. Write the numbers in order. ➡ Draw the blocks. Make them all the same width. ➡ Leave a gap between the bars.

This is a **horizontal** bar chart.

You can draw a **vertical** bar chart like this:

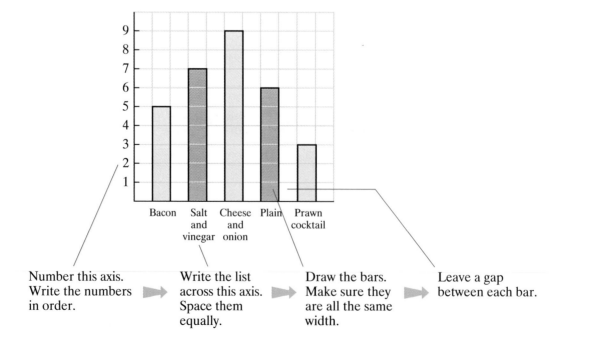

Number this axis. Write the numbers in order. ➡ Write the list across this axis. Space them equally. ➡ Draw the bars. Make sure they are all the same width. ➡ Leave a gap between each bar.

Exercise 14G

1 Draw a bar chart to show the data you collected in Exercise **14A**.

2 Draw a bar chart to show the data you collected in Exercise **14B**.

3 Conduct a survey into the favourite pop stars in your class.
   Draw a bar chart to show the data you collected.

14.8 Reading bar charts

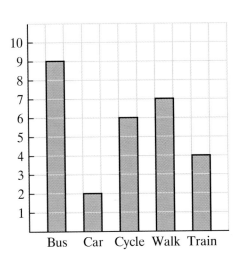

This bar chart shows how class 7B get to school each day:

Most people use the bus: 9 people in all.

6 people cycle.

2 people come by car.

You can find the total number in the survey by adding the heights of all the bars together:

$$9 + 2 + 6 + 7 + 4 = 28$$

There were 28 people in the survey.

Exercise 14H

1 The barchart shows the number of people away in a class each day.

   (a) How many people were away on Tuesday?

   (b) Which day were the most people away?

   (c) What was the total number away in the week?

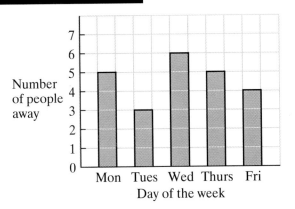

2   The barchart shows which
    newspaper people prefer:

    (a) How many people
        prefer
        (i) the Mail
        (ii) the Sun
        (iii) the Mirror?

    (b) Which was the most
        popular newspaper?

    (c) How many people took
        part in the survey?

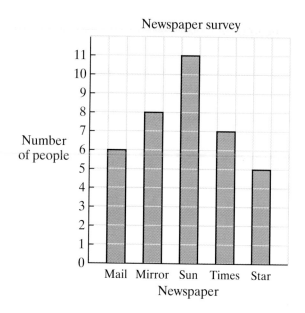

14.9 Using a scale

If you have a lot of people in
your survey the blocks will be
too long for the page.

You need to use a scale.

The most common scales are:

Go up in 2s ├─┼─┼─┼─┼─┼─┼─┤   Use this for totals up to 20.
             0 2 4 6 8 10 12 14

Go up in 5s ├─┼─┼─┼─┼─┼─┼─┤   Use this for totals up to 50.
             0 5 10 15 20 25 30 35

Go up in 10s ├─┼─┼─┼─┼─┼─┼─┤   Use this for totals up to 100.
             0 10 20 30 40 50 60 70

Example 6

The number of letters delivered to an office one week was:

Mon	Tue	Wed	Thur	Fri	Sat
16	8	20	17	11	4

Draw a bar chart to show this data.

The highest total is 20 so go up in 2s.

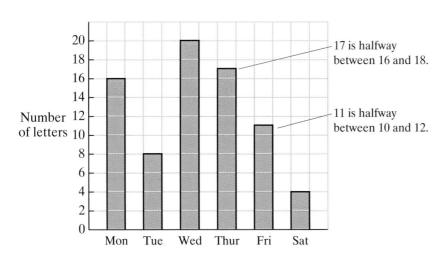

17 is halfway between 16 and 18.

11 is halfway between 10 and 12.

Exercise 14I

1 The number of letters delivered to a Corner Shop one week was:

Mon	Tues	Wed	Thur	Fri
23	16	27	19	21

Draw a bar chart to represent this data.

2 Here are the results of a traffic survey.

Vehicle	Frequency
Cars	17
Lorries	12
Vans	16
Motor Bikes	6
Buses	4
Pedal cycles	2

Show the results on a bar chart.

3 This bar chart shows the frequency of the eight most used letters in a piece of French.

The 8 most frequent letters in a piece of French

(a) Which letter was most frequent?

(b) How many times did **(i)** 'A' **(ii)** 'L' appear?

(c) What are the six most frequent letters in this piece of French?

4 Mark asked each pupil in year 7 how many books they read last month.
Here are his results:

(a) How many pupils read no books?

(b) How many pupils read just one book?

(c) How many pupils read three books?

(d) How many pupils took part in the book-reading survey?

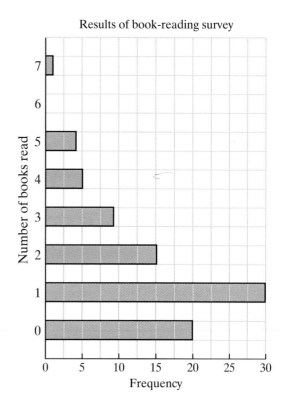

Results of book-reading survey

Summary of key points

1   Data is another word for information.

2   You can collect data using a survey.

3   You can collect data from an experiment.

4   You can use a tally chart to organize data.

Flavour	Tally	Total
Bacon	IIII	5
Salt and vinegar	IIII II	7
Cheese and onion	IIII IIII	9
Plain	IIII I	6
Prawn cocktail	III	3
		30

Bunch the tally marks in 5s. Then they are easier to count.

Count up the tally marks. Put the total here.

Count up all the totals to check you have used all the data
$5 + 7 + 9 + 6 + 3 = 30.$

5   A pictogram uses pictures to show data.

Apple	
Banana	
Orange	
Strawberry	
Peach	
Nectarine	

stands for 2 people

6   A bar chart uses bars or blocks to show data.

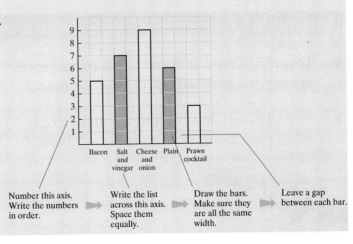

Number this axis. Write the numbers in order.

Write the list across this axis. Space them equally.

Draw the bars. Make sure they are all the same width.

Leave a gap between each bar.

15 Percentages

15.1 Understanding percentages

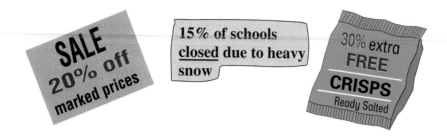

The symbol % means 'per cent'.
Per cent means 'in every 100'.

3% means 3 in every 100.
3% is called a **percentage**.

100% of something is all of it.

Example 1

What percentage is each piece?

There are 10 pieces of chocolate.
Each piece is $100\% \div 10 = 10\%$

There are 4 slices of pizza.
Each slice is $100\% \div 4 = 25\%$

Exercise 15A

1   This chocolate bar is cut into 5 equal pieces.
    What percentage of the bar is each piece?

2   This pie has been cut into 4 equal pieces.
    What percentage of the pie is each piece?

3 Write down the percentage of each shape that is shaded.

(a)   **(b)** 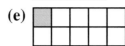 **(c)**

(d)   **(e)**  **(f)**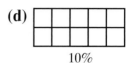

4 Copy each diagram into your book. Shade the percentage.

(a) 50%   **(b)** 25%   **(c)** 20%   **(d)** 10%

15.2 More than one part

Example 2

Jenny eats 3 pieces of this chocolate bar.
What percentage does she eat?

There are 4 pieces of chocolate.
Each piece is 100% ÷ 4 = 25%.

So 3 pieces are 3 × 25% of the bar = 75%

Exercise 15B

1 This chocolate bar has 10 pieces.
What percentage is:

(a) 1 piece
(b) 7 pieces
(c) 3 pieces?

2 This pie has been cut into 5 pieces.
What percentage is:

(a) 1 piece
(b) 3 pieces
(c) 2 pieces
(d) 4 pieces?

3 For each shape, write down the percentage shaded.

(a) **(b)** 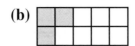 **(c)**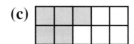

(d) **(e)**  **(f)**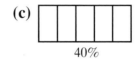

4 Copy these diagrams.
Shade the required percentage.

(a)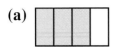
60%

(b)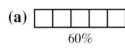
50%

(c)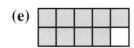
40%

Hint: work out
what percentage
each part is.

(d)
70%

(e)
80%

15.3 Writing percentages as fractions

This square has 100 equal parts.

23 parts 'out of 100' are shaded.
This is 23%

You can write this
as a fraction:

$$\frac{23}{100}$$

23 — 23 parts shaded

100 — 100 parts altogether

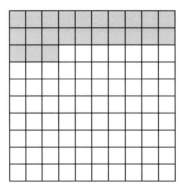

$\frac{23}{100}$ and 23% represent
the same amount.

■ **A percentage can be written as a fraction with the denominator (bottom) 100.**

For example, $23\% = \frac{23}{100}$

Exercise 15C

For each 100 square write down:
(a) the fraction shaded   **(b)** the percentage shaded.

1 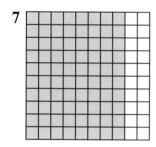   **2** 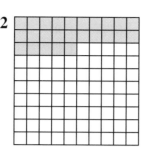   **3**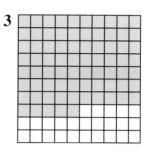

4 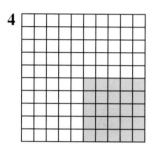   **5** 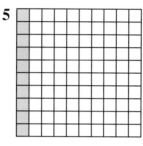   **6**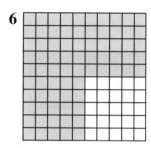

7 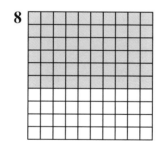   **8** 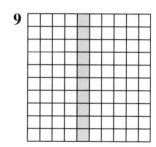   **9**

10   Using a hundred square, shade in:
     (a) 20%   **(b)** 60%   **(c)** 75%   **(d)** 25%   **(e)** 50%

15.4 Writing percentages as decimals

Percentages can also be written as decimals.
     7% means $\frac{7}{100}$.
This can be written as $7 \div 100 = 0.07$
     $7\% = 0.07$

25% means 25 out of 100.
     $25\% = 25 \div 100 = 0.25$

Example 3

Change these percentages to decimals:

(a) 37%   **(b)** 40%   **(c)** 5%

(a) 37% = 37 ÷ 100
37% = 0.37

(b) 40% = 40 ÷ 100
40% = 0.40
= 0.4

Remember: you
can leave off the
zero.

(c) 5% = 5 ÷ 100
5% = 0.05

■ **To change a percentage to a decimal divide by 100.**

For example 23% = 23 ÷ 100 = 0.23

Exercise 15D

Change these percentages to decimals:

1 25%	**2** 36%	**3** 6%	**4** 18%
5 30%	**6** 50%	**7** 8%	**8** 75%
9 62%	**10** 5%	**11** 27%	**12** 54%
13 99%	**14** 70%	**15** 35%	**16** 1%
17 15%	**18** 60%	**19** 120%	**20** 150%

Summary of key points

1 A percentage can be written as a fraction with the denominator (bottom) 100.
For example, $23\% = \frac{23}{100}$.

2 To change a percentage to a decimal divide by 100.
For example 23% = 23 ÷ 100 = 0.23

16 Using and applying mathematics

This unit shows you how to use mathematics to **investigate** a problem.

The problem

Hop and Step

Lucy and her friends are playing a game called Hop and Step.

They have put a green hoop and a red hoop on the floor with some blue hoops in between.

To play the game, Lucy starts in the green hoop. She must finish in the red hoop.

There are three rules to the game:

Rule 1 She can only move forwards towards the red hoop.

Rule 2 She can take a step. This moves her one hoop forward.

Rule 3 She can take a hop. This moves her two hoops forward.

Investigate the number of different ways of getting from the green hoop to the red hoop as the number of blue hoops changes.

Understand the problem

The first thing to do is make sure you understand the problem.
The best way to do this is just have a go.

Example 1

Suppose there are four blue hoops.
Find three different ways of getting from the green hoop to the red hoop.

Remember to follow the rules.

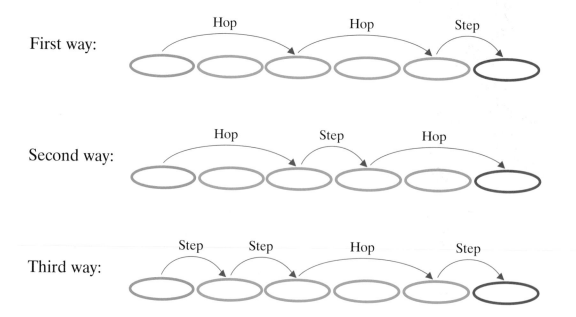

Exercise 16A

Show that there are 8 different ways of getting from the green hoop to the red hoop when there are 4 blue hoops.

Make the problem as simple as you can

Once you understand the problem try to make it as simple as you can.

The simplest game is when there are **zero** blue hoops:

There is only one way of getting to the red hoop: one step.

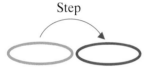

The next simplest game is when there is **one** blue hoop:

There are two ways of getting to the red hoop: one hop or two steps.

Exercise 16B

1   Put two blue hoops between the green and red hoops.
   (a) List all the ways of getting from the green to the red hoop.
   (b) How many different ways are there of getting from the green to the red hoop?

2   Put three blue hoops between the green and red hoop.
    Show that there are five different ways of getting from
    the green to the red hoop.

Organize your approach

As the number of blue hoops increases, you need to
organize your approach to be sure you find all the ways of
getting from the green to the red hoop.

An organized approach to a problem is called a **strategy**.

Here is one strategy you could use:

Do as many hops as you can.

Reduce the number of hops by one.

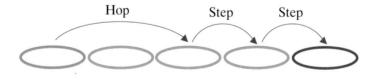

Reduce the number of hops by one again.

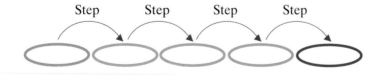

Using a strategy means you are more likely to find **all** the
ways of getting from green to red.

You can shorten the words like this:

Let   S   stand for Step

And H   stand for Hop.

The moves for three blue hoops are:

HH   2 Hops   0 Steps

HSS ⎫
SHS ⎬ 1 Hop   2 Steps
SSH ⎭

SSSS   0 Hops   4 Steps

When there are three blue hoops there are
5 different ways of getting from green to red.

Notice how the H
appears to move
along a diagonal:

H   S   S
S   H   S
S   S   H

The strategy helps
you spot patterns.

<hr>

Exercise 16C

Use your strategy to show that there are 8 different ways of
getting from the green to the red hoop when there are
4 blue hoops.

Record your results

So far you should know that the number of ways of getting
from the green to the red hoop is:

1 when there are 0 blue hoops

2 when there is   1 blue hoop

3 when there are 2 blue hoops

5 when there are 3 blue hoops

8 when there are 4 blue hoops

A good way to keep your results is in a table:

Number of blue hoops	Number of ways of getting from green to red
0	1
1	2
2	3

Exercise 16D

Copy and complete the table:

Number of blue hoops	Number of ways of getting from green to red
0	1
1	2
2	3
3	
4	

Make predictions

Once you have some results and have recorded them in a table you can try to predict what will happen next.

Use your table of results to see if you can spot a pattern:

Number of blue hoops	Number of ways of getting from green to red
0	1
1	2
2	3
3	5
4	8

You should be able to see that:

The number of ways increases as the number of blue hoops increases.

You can predict that there will be more than 8 ways when there are 5 hoops.

If you just look at the number of ways you might spot that there is a pattern:

Number of blue hoops	Number of ways of getting from green to red	Even or odd?
0	1	Odd
1	2	Even
2	3	Odd
3	5	Odd
4	8	Even

You can predict that the pattern will continue like this:

Odd, Even, Odd, Odd, Even, Odd, Odd, Even, Odd, Odd, Even …

This part repeats.

Your prediction could be:
There are an odd number of ways when there are 5 hoops.
There are an odd number of ways when there are 6 hoops.

Exercise 16E

Predict whether there will be an odd or an even number of ways when there are:
(a) 7 blue hoops **(b)** 10 blue hoops **(c)** 20 blue hoops

Try to predict the next number

The point of making a prediction is to find the number of ways without having to play the game.

You can predict that there is an odd number of ways when there are 5 blue hoops.
But the best prediction is exactly how many ways there are.

To predict how many ways there are with 5 blue hoops you need to find a pattern in the numbers.

It helps to write the number of ways like this:

| 1 | 2 | 3 | 5 | 8 | ? |

You need to spot that:
To find the next number in the sequence, add the previous two numbers together.

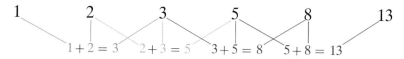

The pattern suggests that the number of ways when there are 5 blue hoops is 13.

You can predict that there are 13 ways when there are 5 hoops.

Hint: if you can't spot a pattern, play the game a few more times to get some more results.

Test your prediction

Now you have a prediction, you must test it to see if it works.

This means you use your strategy to show there are 13 ways when there are 5 blue hoops.

Exercise 16F

1   Show that there are 13 ways of getting from the green to the red hoop when there are 5 blue hoops.

2   Make and test a prediction for the number of ways when there are 6 blue hoops.

Make a generalization

Once you have tested your prediction and it works, you can use your prediction to generalize.
This means giving a rule that always works.

The rule for this sequence of numbers is:

To find the next number in the sequence, add the previous two numbers together.

You can use this generalization to make further predictions if you are still unsure:

Remember: this sequence is called a Fibonacci sequence. You can find out more on page 55.

Number of blue hoops	Number of ways of getting from green to red
0	1
1	2
2	3
3	5
4	8
5	13
6	21
7	34

$8 + 13 = 21$

$13 + 21 = 34$

Exercise 16G

Use your generalization to work out the number of ways when there are:

(a) 8 blue hoops

(b) 9 blue hoops

(c) 10 blue hoops

(d) 15 blue hoops

Now use all the steps again to play this version of Hop and Step:

Lucy plays a new game of Hop and Step.
This time the rules are the same except:

a hop takes her 3 hoops forward.

- Investigate the number of different ways of getting from the green hoop to the red hoop as the number of blue hoops changes.

- Try to find a new generalization.

- Use your generalization to find the number of ways when there are 10 blue hoops.

Summary of key points

For any investigation

- Understand the problem – have a go.
- Make the problem as simple as you can
- Organize your approach – use a strategy
- Record your results – use a table
- Make predictions – try to predict the next number
- Test your prediction
- Make a generalization

17 Calculators and computers

This unit shows you some ways of using scientific calculators, graphical calculators and computers to help solve mathematical problems.

The examples will work on Casio calculators and most computers. Your teacher will tell you if you need to change any of the instructions.

17.1 Using your memory

You can use the memory on a scientific calculator to help you work with money or lists.

Example 1

Janet's money box contains twenty three 1p coins, seventeen 2p coins, nine 5p coins, and thirteen 10p coins. How much money has she saved?

Press

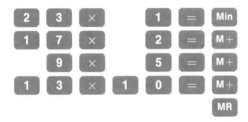

Answer: 232 pence which is £2.32

Exercise 17A   Scientific calculator

1   Lucy buys these stamps from the Post Office: 8 second class stamps at 20p, 22 first class stamps at 26p, 3 stamps at 37p, and 2 stamps at 43p. Find the total cost and the change she receives if she pays with a £10 note.

2   In one week a school tuck shop sold 83 bars of chocolate at 42p each, 229 cans of squash at 35p each and 355 packets of crisps at 15p each. Find the total takings for the week.

Find these keys on your scientific calculator:

Min this key puts a new number into memory

M+ adds a number to the memory

M− subtracts a number from the memory

MR recalls (brings back) from memory

AC clears the calculator display

AC **Min** clears the memory

3 Michael bought 17 Christmas cards at 5p each, 12 cards at 9p each and 5 cards at 14p each. How much did he spend on cards?

4 Suwani does a 6 mile sponsored walk. Twenty nine people sponsor her at 2p per mile, thirteen people at 5p per mile, and twelve people at 10p per mile. How much will she collect if she completes the whole distance?

17.2 Square numbers and number chains

You can find square numbers using the key $\boxed{x^2}$

Example 2

Find **(a)** 5^2 **(b)** 7^2 **(c)** 13^2

(a) Press $\boxed{5}$ $\boxed{x^2}$ Answer: 25

(b) Press $\boxed{7}$ $\boxed{x^2}$ Answer: 49

(c) Press $\boxed{1}$ $\boxed{3}$ $\boxed{x^2}$ Answer: 169

The $\boxed{x^2}$ key multiplies a number by itself.

Multiplying a number by itself gives a **square number**

$5 \times 5 = 25$

A short way to write 5×5 is 5^2

You say '5 squared'

Exercise 17B

1 Calculate 9^2.

2 Calculate 12^2.

3 Calculate 17^2.

4 Calculate $5^2 + 12^2$.

5 Calculate $6^2 + 8^2$.

Number chains

You can make a number chain by using a simple rule.

Example 3

Start with 44   Follow this rule:
'square and add the digits of the previous number'

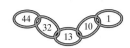

$$44 \rightarrow 4^2 + 4^2 = 16 + 16 = 32$$
$$32 \rightarrow 3^2 + 2^2 = 9 + 4 = 13$$
$$13 \rightarrow 1^2 + 3^2 = 1 + 9 = 10$$
$$10 \rightarrow 1^2 + 0^2 = 1 + 0 = 1$$
$$1 \rightarrow 1^2 = 1 \quad \text{STOP when you get a number which is already in the chain}$$

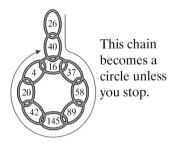

This chain becomes a circle unless you stop.

Number chain: $44 \rightarrow 32 \rightarrow 13 \rightarrow 10 \rightarrow 1$

Exercise 17C

1   Square and add the digits starting with 19.

2   Square and add the digits starting with 49.

3   Square and add the digits starting with 82.

4   Square and add the digits starting with 15.

17.3 Ordering whole numbers and decimals using random numbers

Most calculators and computer programs can produce **random numbers**. These are usually decimals with three digits. For example:

   0.348   0.846   0.962   0.137

sometimes they have fewer digits:

   0.7   0.86   0.29   0.04

Find out how to make your calculator produce random numbers.

Random means all numbers have an equal chance of being produced.

Exercise 17D   Scientific calculator

1   Find the Rn# or Ran# key.
You may have to press INV or SHIFT first.
Produce 20 random decimal numbers and write them down.

2   **A game for two players**   Each player draws this number grid:

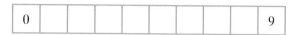

- Take turns to produce a random number.
- Look at the last digit.
- Write it in the right place on your grid.

The first person to collect all the digits from 0 to 9 wins.

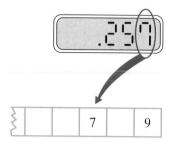

3   Repeat the game using this grid:

- Collect the last **two** digits of each random number.
- Write them on your grid.

The first person to fill their grid wins.
But all the numbers must be in order:

0	15	28	41	49	52	68	74	81	99

DON'T put this here …

… or every number to its left must be less than 19!

4   Repeat the game using this grid:

0									1

- Use **all three** digits of each random number, including the decimal point

Remember: **0.428** is less than **0.43** is less than **0.5**

Random numbers by computer

You can write a computer program in BASIC to produce random decimal numbers. One of these programs should work on your computer:

```
10 REPEAT            DO
20 PRINT RND         PRINT RND
30 LET Z = GET       LET Z = GET
40 UNTIL FALSE       LOOP
50 END               END
```

Press the *Space bar* to see the next random number.

Press *Escape* or *Ctrl·Break* to stop the programs.

Exercise 17E   BASIC

1   Type and save the program on your computer.

2   Produce 10 random decimal numbers by running the program. Write them down.

3   Edit the program so the line:

```
PRINT RND
```

becomes:

```
PRINT INT(10*RND)
```

Run the new program to produce 20 random whole numbers between 0 and 9.

Write your numbers down.

4   Repeat the game from question 3, page 234 but use the BASIC program with the line:

```
PRINT INT(100*RND)
```

This produces random whole numbers from 0 to 99.

5   Repeat the game using this grid:

0							1

Use the BASIC program with this line:

```
PRINT (INT(100*RND))/100
```

This produces random two-digit decimal numbers. Use all the digits and the decimal point. For example:

0	.17	.2	.39	.61	.69	.7	.88	.97	1

17.4 Multiplication tables practice

The next page shows some ways to practise your times tables using random numbers:

Exercise 17F   Scientific calculator

1   Seven times table

- Press the `Rn#` or `Ran#` key and write down the *last digit* of your random number.
  Ignore 0 or 1 when they occur.
- *Without using a calculator* multiply this random digit by 7 and write down your result.
- Repeat this 20 times, then check your answers using the calculator.

7 times table		
random number	my result	check
7	49	✓
2	14	✓
4	27	✗
5	40	✗

2   Now try other multiplication tables.

Exercise 17G   Graphical calculator

1   Six times table

- Produce a random whole number from 2 to 12 by pressing the keys:

  `Int` `1` `1` `Ran#` `+` `2` `EXE`

  and write it down.
- *Without using a calculator* multiply this random number by 6 and write down your result.
- Keep pressing `EXE` to repeat this 20 times, then check your answers using the calculator.

6 times table		
random number	my result	check
10	60	✓
3	18	✓
12	60	✗
5	30	✓

2   Now try other multiplication tables.

Exercise 17H   BASIC

1   Type and save this program on your computer:

```
10 FOR X=1 TO 20
20 PRINT INT(11*RND+2);" x 8 = ?"
30 LET Z=GET
40 NEXT X
50 END
```

2 **Eight times table**

- Run the program.
- *Without using a calculator*, do the multiplication and write down your result.
- Keep pressing the *Space bar* to repeat this 20 times, then check your answers using a calculator.

$2 \times 8 = ?$
$10 \times 8 = ?$
$12 \times 8 = ?$
$7 \times 8 = ?$
$3 \times 8 = ?$

3 Now try other multiplication tables.

Exercise 17I **Spreadsheet**

1 Type this formula into cell A1 of a new spreadsheet:

`=INT(11*RAND()+2)`

This will display a random whole number from 2 to 12. Write this number down.

- *Without using a calculator*, multiply this random number by 9 and write down your result.
- Do a manual recalculation of the spreadsheet to repeat this 20 times, then check your answers using a calculator.

2 Now try other multiplication tables.

3 Start a new spreadsheet. Follow these instructions carefully:

In cell A1 type the formula `=INT(11*RAND()+2)`
Copy cell A1 down column A as far as cell A15

In cell B1 type the letter `"x"`
Copy cell B1 down column B as far as cell B15

In cell C1 type the formula `=INT(11*RAND()+2)`
In cell C2 type the formula `=C$1`
Copy cell C2 down column C as far as cell C15

In cell D1 type `" ="`
Copy cell D1 down column D as far as cell D15

Move to a column which you cannot see at the moment, for example column K
In cell K1 type the formula `=A1*C1`
Copy cell K1 down column K as far as cell K15

Most spreadsheets are set up to do automatic recalculation.

Find out how to make your spreadsheet do manual recalculation.

Then it will only do calculations when you press a key (like **F9** in Excel).

Put a *space* before the *equals* sign

Move back to column A so that you cannot see the numbers in column K

Now you are ready to begin!

- Do a manual recalculation of the spreadsheet. It will show times table questions:

Do another manual recalculation and repeat the process.

	A	B	C	D	E	F	G	H	I	J	K
1	5	x	12	=							60
2	2	x	12	=							24
3	9	x	12	=							108
4	3	x	12	=							36
5	8	x	12	=							96
6	9	x	12	=							108
7	6	x	12	=							72
8	7	x	12	-							84

- *Without using a calculator,* work out the answers and type them in column E

- Move to column K to check your answers

Clear column E then have another go!

17.5 Recycling machines and number sequences

This recycling machine adds 2 to each input number.

If the first input is 1 the output is 3.

Then 3 is the second input and the output is 5.

The **sequence** of numbers produced in this way begins 1, 3, 5, 7, 9 ... (the odd numbers).

You can use the constant function on your calculator to produce number sequences like this.

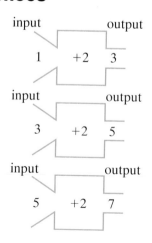

Exercise 17J   Scientific calculator

Write down the first five numbers in each of these sequences:

1 [2] [+] [+] [1] [=] [=] [=] ...   (add 2)

2 [3] [+] [+] [4] [=] [=] [=] ...   (add 3)

3 [2] [×] [×] [3] [=] [=] [=] ...   (multiply by 2)

4 [5] [−] [−] [6] [0] [=] [=] [=] ...   (subtract 5)

5 [2] [÷] [÷] [6] [4] [=] [=] [=] ...   (divide by 2)

This two step recycling machine multiplies by 2 then subtracts 3.

If the first input is 4 the output is 5.

Then 5 is the second input and the output is 7.

This sequence begins   4,   5,   7,   11,   19   ...

You can use the answer memory on a graphical calculator to produce these number sequences.

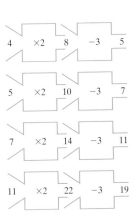

Exercise 17K   Graphical calculator

Write down the first five numbers in each of these sequences:

1 [4] [EXE] [Ans] [×] [2] [−] [3] [EXE] [EXE] ...

2 [2] [EXE] [Ans] [×] [3] [+] [1] [EXE] [EXE] ...

3 [7] [EXE] [Ans] [×] [2] [−] [1] [EXE] [EXE] ...

4 [7] [8] [4] [EXE] [Ans] [÷] [2] [+] [8] [EXE] [EXE] ...

5 What two step machine produces the sequence:
   5,   13,   29,   61,   125   ... ?

6 What two step machine produces the sequence:
   13,   21,   37,   69,   133   ... ?

17.6 Symmetry in LOGO

You can use the computer program LOGO to help you understand rotational symmetry and line (reflective) symmetry.

First type the following three procedures:

```
TO SQUARE
REPEAT 4[FD 50 RT 90]
END
```

```
TO RFLAG
FD 50 SQUARE BK 50
END
```

```
TO LFLAG
FD 50 LT 90 SQUARE RT 90 BK 50
END
```

Find out which version of LOGO you are using.

The instructions given here are written for MSWLogo

Example 4

Type CS HT PD REPEAT 4[RFLAG RT 90]
This shape has rotational symmetry of order 4.
There are no lines of reflective symmetry.

Example 5

Type CS HT PD REPEAT 2[RFLAG LFLAG RT 180]
This shape has rotational symmetry of order 2.
There are 2 lines of reflective symmetry.

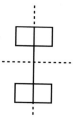

Exercise 17L

Type the following LOGO commands on your computer then draw each shape in your book.

Write down whether each shape has rotational symmetry.

Draw any lines of reflective symmetry.

1 CS HT PD REPEAT 3[RFLAG RT 120]

2 CS HT PD REPEAT 2[RFLAG RT 90 LFLAG RT 90]

Find out how to *save*, *load* and *edit* LOGO procedures

3   CS HT PD REPEAT 8[RFLAG RT 45]

4   CS HT PD REPEAT 3[RFLAG LFLAG RT 120]

5   CS HT PD REPEAT 4[SQUARE RT 90]

6   CS HT PD LFLAG SQUARE

7   CS HT PD REPEAT 2[LFLAG SQUARE RT 90]

8   CS HT REPEAT 8[PU FD 50 PD SQUARE PU BK 50
RT 45]

17.7 Angles practice in LOGO

You can use the computer program LOGO to help you draw
and estimate angles. You will need the following three
short procedures Q, H and A:

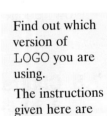

```
TO Q
MAKE "B RANDOM  90 CS HT PD
MAKE "A RANDOM 360 SETH :A
MAKE "D SIGN (180 . :A)
SETPC [255 0 0]
FD 120  BK 120
REPEAT  :B [FD 30 BK 30 RT :D]
FD 120  BK 120
END


TO H
SETPC [0 255 0]  SETH :A
REPEAT 12 [FD 60 BK 60 RT 30]
END


TO A
SHOW :B
END
```

Find out which
version of
LOGO you are
using.

The instructions
given here are
written for
MSWLogo

Procedure Q draws a *new angle* for you to estimate. If you
need *help* use procedure H. The *answer* is given by
procedure A.

Find out how to
save, and *load*
LOGO
procedures.

Exercise 17M

1   Type and save the procedures Q, H and A.

2   Use procedure Q to draw a new angle, then
    try to estimate the size of the angle in degrees.
    Write down your estimate.
    If you need help use procedure H.
    Check your estimate with procedure A.
    Write down the computer's answer.
    Repeat this for another 9 angles.

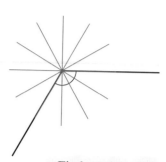

Find out how to
edit procedures
in LOGO

3   Edit procedure Q so that the line

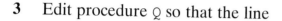

```
            MAKE "B RANDOM   90 CS HT PD
becomes   MAKE "B RANDOM  180 CS HT PD
```

Now repeat question 2.

4   Edit procedure Q so that the line

```
            MAKE "B RANDOM 180 CS HT PD
becomes   MAKE "B RANDOM 270 CS HT PD
```

Now repeat question 2.

17.8 Charts and graphs from data using a spreadsheet

Computer spreadsheets can produce a selection of different
charts and graphs, so it can be very useful to use a
spreadsheet for storing your data.

Find out how to
produce bar
charts and line
graphs from
data in your
computer
spreadsheet.

Look for
horizontal bar
charts, vertical
bar charts and
line graphs.

Exercise 17N

1   The daily temperature (minimum and maximum) and
    monthly rainfall figures for Monkey Bay in Malawi are
    shown opposite. Type this data into your spreadsheet
    and save it.

	A	B	C	D
1	**Month**	**Min Temp °C**	**Max Temp °C**	**Rainfall mm**
2	Jan	23	28	325
3	Feb	22	28	315
4	Mar	21	29	400
5	Apr	20	29	140
6	May	18	26	40
7	Jun	16	25	10
8	Jul	15	25	5
9	Aug	16	26	2
10	Sep	18	29	3
11	Oct	21	32	5
12	Nov	24	32	60
13	Dec	23	30	225

2 Display the
rainfall data
in a line graph
like this:

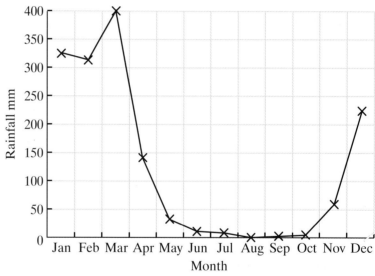

3 Display the
temperature data
in a bar chart like this:

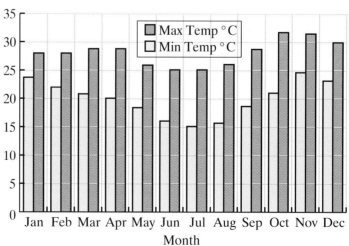

Index